KT-230-218

TENSIONS

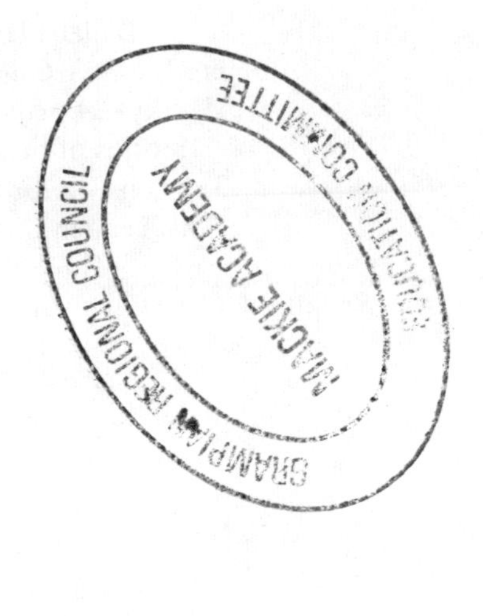
GRAMPIAN REGIONAL COUNCIL
EDUCATION COMMITTEE
MACKIE ACADEMY

THE SECONDARY ENGLISH PROGRAMME

General Editor: W. A. Gatherer

Ballads High and Low
Here Lies – *A Collection of Comic Verse*
My Sky – *A Sequence of Lyric Poems*
Stories of the American West
Tensions – *A Group of Short Stories*
The Tender Conspiracy – *A Novel*
Three Short Plays
Worlds Of Their Own – *A Collection of Humorous Writings*

Tensions

A Group of Short Stories

presented by

ROBERT MILLAR
formerly Director of the Centre for Information in the Teaching of English, Edinburgh

HEINEMANN EDUCATIONAL BOOKS
LONDON

Heinemann Educational Books Ltd
LONDON EDINBURGH MELBOURNE AUCKLAND
TORONTO HONG KONG SINGAPORE
KUALA LUMPUR IBADAN NAIROBI
JOHANNESBURG LUSAKA NEW DELHI

ISBN 0 435 10377 6

First published 1975

Set in 11/12 Monophoto Times

Published by
Heinemann Educational Books Ltd
48 Charles Street, London W1X 8AH
Photoset and printed in Malta
by St Paul's Press Ltd

Contents

	page
List of Illustrations	7
About this book	9
Texts – 1	
A Message from the Pig-Man by John Wain	11
READING AIDS – 1	19
STUDY AIDS – 1	20
What is a Short Story?	20
Components of the Short Story:	20
Character	20
Action, Plot, Incident	20
Background, Setting	21
Speech, Dialogue	21
Theme	21
Method of Narration	21
Language	22
Structure	22
Commentary: *A Message from the Pig-Man*	22
PROJECTIONS – 1	26
Texts – 2	
First Confession by Frank O'Connor	28
READING AIDS – 2	38
STUDY AIDS – 2	39
Commentary: *First Confession*	39
PROJECTIONS – 2	43
Texts – 3	
On Saturday Afternoon by Alan Sillitoe	44

READING AIDS – 3 52

STUDY AIDS – 3 53
Commentary: *On Saturday Afternoon* 53

PROJECTIONS – 3 57

Texts – 4
You Should Have Seen the Mess by Muriel Spark 59

READING AIDS – 4 67

STUDY AIDS – 4 67
Commentary: *You Should Have Seen the Mess* 67

PROJECTIONS – 4 70

Acknowledgements 72

List of Illustrations

The copyright-holders permission to reproduce these is gratefully acknowledged.

	page
Dustman in alley way (Lorentz Gullachsen)	13
Man in cloth cap (Camera Press, photo by Studio Gallery, Stockholm)	17
Grandmother (Keystone Press)	28
Candle and half-crown (Lorentz Gullachsen)	30
Boy and priest in the confessional box (Lorentz Gullachsen)	34
Oldham (Camera Press, photo by Ken Lambert)	44
Noose (Lorentz Gullachsen)	48
Girl in office (Camera Press)	60
Cottage (Camera Press)	63
Artist's studio (Camera Press, photograph by Hugh Sibley)	66

Cover – Lorentz Gullachsen

About this Book

The short stories in this book are all about certain aspects of the lives of young people. I have selected them for various reasons. The first reason is that I am sure that reading them will be enjoyable, for they are sometimes amusing, sometimes moving, and all interesting in some way. A second reason is that they are all *good*: that is, they are well written, they have something important to say, and they are all by well-known and expert writers.

Since the Second World War, the short story has become a very significant form of fiction. The best short story writers have held the mirror faithfully to ordinary, everyday life, and they have been able to show us much that is interesting and important in their studies of social habits and character. These stories are more than first-rate entertainment – though they are that. They are also explorations into the nature of young people and their problems and outlooks. It will help you to understand other people to read these stories with care and attention; but it will also help you to understand yourself.

The READING AIDS will help you to understand the text as you read through it. The STUDY AIDS will help you to appreciate the story as a work of literature, and will give you deeper insight into the craft of the writer. The PROJECTIONS will give you further experience and enjoyment of writing, discussing and analysing various kinds of composition.

ROBERT MILLAR

A Message from the Pig-Man
by John Wain

He was never called Ekky now, because he was getting to be a real boy, nearly six, with grey flannel trousers that had a separate belt and weren't kept up by elastic, and his name was Eric. But this was just one of those changes brought about naturally, by time, not a disturbing alteration; he understood that. His mother hadn't meant that kind of change when she had promised, 'Nothing will be changed.' It was all going to go on as before, except that Dad wouldn't be there, and Donald would be there instead. He knew Donald, of course, and felt all right about his being in the house, though it seemed, when he lay in bed and thought about it, mad and pointless that Donald's coming should mean that Dad had to go. Why should it mean that? The house was quite big. He hadn't any brothers and sisters, and if he *had* had any he wouldn't have minded sharing his bedroom, even with a baby that wanted a lot of looking after, so long as it left the spare room free for Dad to sleep in. If he did that they wouldn't have a spare room, it was true, but, then, the spare room was nearly always empty; the last time anybody had used the spare room was *years* ago, when he had been much smaller—last winter, in fact. And, even then, the visitor, the lady with the funny teeth who laughed as she breathed in, instead of as she breathed out like everyone else, had only stayed two or three nights. *Why* did grown-ups do everything in such a mad, silly way? They often told him not to be silly, but they were silly themselves in a useless way, not laughing or singing or anything, just being silly and sad.

It was so hard to read the signs; that was another thing. When they did give you something to go on, it was impossible to know how to take it. Dad had bought him a train, just a few weeks ago, and taught him how to fit the lines together. That ought to have meant that he would stay; what sensible person would buy a train, and fit it all up ready to run, even as a present for another person—*and then leave*? Donald had been quite good about the train, Eric had to admit that; he had bought a bridge for it and a lot of rolling-stock. At first he had got the wrong kind of rolling-stock, with wheels too close together to fit on to the rails; but instead of playing the usual grown-ups' trick of pulling a face and then not doing anything about it, he had gone back to the shop, straight away that same afternoon, and got the right kind. Perhaps that meant *he* was going to leave. But that didn't seem likely. Not the way Mum held on to him all the time, even holding him round the middle as if he needed keeping in one piece.

All the same, he was not Ekky now, he was Eric, and he was sensible and grown-up. Probably it was his own fault that everything seemed strange. He was not living up to his grey flannel trousers—and perhaps that was it; being afraid of too many things, not asking questions that would probably turn out to have quite simple answers.

The Pig-man, for instance. He had let the Pig-man worry him far too much. None of the grown-ups acted as if the Pig-man was anything to be afraid of. He probably just *looked* funny, that was all. If, instead of avoiding him so carefully, he went outside one evening and looked at him, took a good long, unafraid look, leaving the back door open behind him so that he could dart in to safety and warmth of the house. . .no! It was better, after all, not to see the Pig-man; not till he was bigger, anyway; nearly six was quite big but it wasn't really *very* big. . . .

And yet it was one of those puzzling things. No one ever told him to be careful not to let the Pig-man get hold of him, or warned him in any way; so the Pig-man *must* be harmless, because when it came to anything that *could* hurt you, like the traffic on the main road, people were always ramming it into you that you must look both ways, and all that stuff. And yet when it came to the Pig-man no one ever mentioned him; he seemed beneath the notice of grown-ups. His mother would say, now and then, 'Let me see, it's today the Pig-man comes, isn't it?' or, 'Oh dear, the Pig-man will be coming round soon, and I haven't put anything out.' If she talked like this Eric's spine would tingle and go cold; he would keep very still and wait, because quite often her next words would be, 'Eric, just take these peelings,' or whatever it was, 'out to the bucket, dear, will you?' The bucket was about fifty yards away from the back door; it was shared by the people in the two next-door houses. None of *them* was afraid of the Pig-man, either. What was their attitude? he wondered. Were they sorry for him, having to eat damp old stuff out of a bucket – tea-leaves and eggshells and that sort of thing? Perhaps he cooked it when he got home, and made it a bit nicer. Certainly, it didn't look too nice when you lifted the lid of the bucket and saw it all lying there. It sometimes smelt, too. Was the

Pig-man very poor? Was he sorry for himself, or did he feel all right about being like that? *Like what?* What did the Pig-man look like? He would have little eyes, and a snout with a flat end; but would he have trotters, or hands and feet like a person's?

Lying on his back, Eric worked soberly at the problem. The Pig-man's bucket had a handle; so he must carry it in the ordinary way, in his hand – unless, of course, he walked on all fours and carried it in his mouth. But that wasn't very likely, because if he walked on all fours what difference would there be between him and an ordinary pig? To be called the Pig-man, rather than the Man-pig, surely implied that he was upright, and dressed. Could he talk? Probably, in a kind of grunting way, or else how could he tell the people what kind of food he wanted them to put in his bucket? *Why hadn't he asked Dad about the Pig-man?* That had been his mistake; Dad would have told him exactly all about it. But he had gone. Eric fell asleep, and in his sleep he saw Dad and the Pig-man going in a train together; he called, but they did not hear and the train carried them away. 'Dad!' he shouted desperately after it. 'Don't bring the Pig-man when you come back! Don't bring the Pig-man!' Then his mother was in the room, kissing him and smelling nice; she felt soft, and the softness ducked him into sleep, this time without dreams; but the next day his questions returned.

Still, there was school in the morning, and going down to the swings in the afternoon, and altogether a lot of different things to crowd out the figure of the Pig-man and the questions connected with him. And Eric was never farther from worrying about it all than that moment, a few evenings later, when it suddenly came to a crisis.

Eric had been allowed, 'just for once', to bring his train into the dining-room after tea, because there was a fire there that made it nicer than the room where he usually played. It was warm and bright, and the carpet in front of the fireplace was smooth and firm, exactly right for laying out the rails on. Donald had come home and was sitting – in Dad's chair, but never mind – reading the paper and smoking. Mum was in the kitchen, clattering gently about, and both doors were open so that she and Donald could call out remarks to each other. Only a short passage lay between. It was just the part of the day Eric liked best, and bed-time was comfortably far off. He fitted the sections of rail together, glancing in anticipation at the engine as it stood proudly waiting to haul the carriages round and round, tremendously fast.

Then his mother called: 'Eric! Do be a sweet boy, and take this stuff out for the Pig-man. My hands are covered with cake mixture. I'll let you scrape out the basin when you come in.'

For a moment he kept quite still, hoping he hadn't really heard her say it, that it was just a voice inside his head. But Donald looked over at him and said: 'Go along, old man. You don't mind, do you?'

Eric said, 'But tonight's when the Pig-man *comes.*'

Surely, *surely* they weren't asking him to go out, in the deep twilight, just at the time when there was the greatest danger of actually *meeting* the Pig-man?

'All the better,' said Donald, turning back to his paper.

Why was it better? Did they *want* him to meet the Pig-man?

Slowly, wondering why his feet and legs didn't refuse to move, Eric went through into the kitchen. 'There it is,' his mother said, pointing to a brown-paper carrier full of potato-peelings and scraps.

He took it up and opened the back door. If he was quick, and darted along to the bucket *at once*, he would be able to lift the lid, throw the stuff in quickly, and be back in the house in about the time it took to count ten.

One – two – three – four – five – six. He stopped. The bucket wasn't there.

It had gone. Eric peered round, but the light, though faint, was not as faint as *that*. He could see that the bucket had gone. *The Pig-man had already been.*

Seven – eight – nine – ten, his steps were joyous and light. Back in the house, where it was warm and bright and his train was waiting.

'The Pig-man's gone, Mum. The bucket's not there.'

She frowned, hands deep in the pudding-basin. 'Oh, yes, I do believe I heard him. But it was only a moment ago. Yes, it was just before I called you, darling. It must have been that that made me think of it.'

'Yes?' he said politely, putting down the carrier.

'So if you nip along, dear, you can easily catch him up. And I *do* want that stuff out of the way.'

'Catch him up?' he asked, standing still in the doorway.

'Yes, dear, *catch him up*,' she answered rather sharply (the Efficient Young Mother knows when to be Firm). 'He can't possibly be more than a very short way down the road.'

Before she had finished Eric was outside the door and running. This was a technique he knew. It was the same as getting into icy-cold water. If it was the end, if the Pig-man seized him by the hand and dragged him off to his hut, well, so much the worse. Swinging the paper carrier in his hand, he ran fast through the dusk.

The back view of the Pig-man was much as he had expected it to be. A slow, rather lurching gait, hunched shoulders, an old hat crushed down on his head (to hide his ears?), and the pail in his hand. Plod, plod, as if he were tired. Perhaps this was just a ruse, though; probably he could pounce quickly enough when his wicked little eyes saw a nice tasty little boy or something . . . did the Pig-man eat birds? Or cats?

Eric stopped. He opened his mouth to call to the Pig-man, but the first time he tried nothing came out except a small rasping squeak. His heart was banging like fireworks going off. He could hardly hear anything.

'Mr Pig-man!' he called, and this time the words came out clear and rather high.

The jogging old figure stopped, turned, and looked at him. Eric could not see properly from where he stood. But he *had* to see. Everything, even his fear, sank and drowned in the raging tide of his curiosity. He moved forward. With each step he saw more clearly. The Pig-man was just an ordinary old man.

'Hello, sonny, Got some stuff there for the old grunters?'

Eric nodded, mutely, and held out his offering. What old grunters? What did he mean?

The Pig-man put down his bucket. He had ordinary hands, ordinary arms. He took the lid off. Eric held out the paper carrier, and the Pig-man's hand actually touched his own for a second. A flood of gratitude rose up inside him. The Pig-man tipped the scraps into the bucket and handed the carrier back.

'Thanks, sonny,' he said.

'Who's it for?' Eric asked, with another rush of articulateness. His voice seemed to have a life of its own.

The Pig-man straightened up, puzzled. Then he laughed, in a gurgling sort of way, but not like a pig at all.

'Arh Aarh Harh Harh,' the Pig-man went. 'Not for me, if that's whatcher mean, arh harh.'

He put the lid back on the bucket. 'It's for the old grunters,' he said. 'The old porkers. Just what they likes. Only not fruit skins. I leaves a note, sometimes, about what not to put in. Never fruit skins.

It gives 'em the belly-ache.'

He was called the Pig-man because he had some pigs that he looked after.

'Thank you,' said Eric. 'Good night.' He ran back towards the house, hearing the Pig-man, the ordinary old man, the ordinary, usual, normal old man, say in his just ordinary old man's voice, 'Good night, sonny.'

So that was how you did it. You just went straight ahead, not worrying about this or that. Like getting into cold water. You just *did* it.

He slowed down as he got to the gate. For instance, if there was a question that you wanted to know the answer to, and you had always just felt you couldn't ask, the thing to do was to ask it. Just straight out, like going up to the Pig-man. Difficult things, troubles, questions, you just treated them like the Pig-man.

So that was it!

The warm light shone through the crack of the door. He opened it and went in. His mother was standing at the table, her hands still working the cake mixture about. She would let him scrape out the basin, and the spoon – he would ask for the spoon, too. But not straight away. There was a more important thing first.

He put the paper carrier down and went up to her. 'Mum,' he said. 'Why can't Dad be with us even if Donald *is* here? I mean, why can't he live with us as well as Donald?'

His mother turned and went to the sink. She put the tap on and held her hands under it.

'Darling,' she called.

'Yes?' came Donald's voice.

'D'you know what he's just said?'

'What?'

'He's just asked . . .' She turned the tap off and dried her hands, not looking at Eric. 'He wants to know why we can't have Jack to live with us.'

There was a silence, then Donald said, quietly, so that his voice only just reached Eric's ears. 'That's a hard one.'

'You can scrape out the basin,' his mother said to Eric. She lifted him up and kissed him. Then she rubbed her cheek along his, leaving a wet smear. 'Poor little Ekky,' she said in a funny voice.

She put him down and he began to scrape out the pudding-basin, certain at least of one thing, that grown-ups were mad and silly and he hated them all, all, *all.*

Reading Aids – 1

page 11: *to read the signs* to get the right answer – here, to know exactly what the behaviour of grown-ups meant.

pulling a face putting on an expression of annoyance or embarrassment.

12 *living up to his grey flannel trousers* being as grown-up in his attitude and understanding as he ought to be.

Eric's spine would tingle and grow cold he would feel symptoms of fear.

14 *trotters* pig's feet.

soberly seriously, solemnly.

ducked him into sleep pushed him down into sleep.

crisis a turning-point.

anticipation looking forward.

15 *scrape out the basin* clean the basin and eat the sweet mixture he could collect from it.

brown-paper carrier carrier bag.

16 *lurching* swaying from side to side.

ruse trick.

rush of articulateness sudden outburst of speech after being tongue-tied.

Study Aids – 1

What is a short story?

Nobody has ever found a satisfactory definition of a short story. So many different kinds of writing have been called 'short stories' that no definition can cover all of them. However, the four stories in this book are fairly similar in many ways; so we can ask ourselves what features are common to them all. By studying these features we can find answers to some important questions. What, if anything, makes a story unique? What is the writer trying to do? What does the writer succeed in doing?

Components of the short story

All our four stories have to do with human beings, what they do and say, and where they perform their actions. So when we approach a story critically we will want to find out what, according to his purpose, the writer has chosen to do about *character*, about *action* and *plot* and *incident*, about *background* and *setting* and about *dialogue* (the words people speak).

CHARACTER

Generally there are very few characters in a short story. These characters are usually chosen because they, and they alone, are important in the story being told. Normally, too, only one character takes up much of our attention. All others are important only so far as they have an effect on the actions, thoughts and feelings of the main or central character. The short story, therefore, presents a little drama of life, and we must notice what effect the characters have on one another. Because the length of a short story is limited, the writer has little chance to create elaborate characters. Apart from the central character the other people are given only those features of personality that affect the main character. Still, the characters can be placed in a certain social class. They can be of a certain age. And they have their own point of view on living. The writer, too, may decide to introduce a wide range of social types or, on the other hand, create characters that are similar in type.

ACTION, PLOT, INCIDENT

Usually, then, there is one main character. Because that main character usually has to undergo some important experience, the writer has to select a number of actions or events that serve to bring about the experience. To achieve the best effect, no irrelevant actions or episodes should be included. Digressions would weaken the effect of the main story. As readers, we must pay attention to the kind of actions chosen by the writer for his purpose. Is he aiming at the realistic, the fantastic, the romantic, the satirical, the sentimental? We must note, too, the time-scale used by the author – whether it is short and the story is concentrated or whether there is a long time-span with a more thinly spread narrative.

In real life it is difficult to see a pattern in the succession of events that takes place. But in a story the writer, as an artist, selects or invents happenings that he feels are significant. These are arranged in a pattern so that life seems to be more meaningful.

Normally the story falls into a more or less recognizable shape. First comes the *exposition* or *opening situation* in which a basis is laid for the story as it affects the central character. The initial situation develops by means of *complications*: those events that have an effect upon the central character so as to make life more difficult for him. The train of difficulties eventually reaches a *crisis* or turning point in the story. In the crisis the central character can no longer escape from the pressure of events and has to face up to the problem, to come to some kind of decision about it. The decision made is important in the character's life, for by dealing with the problem the character undergoes an experience that changes his pattern of living. The new pattern is shown in the *dénouement*.

BACKGROUND, SETTING

We all live in some kind of environment, and our environment has some effect on our characters and actions. So the writer has to decide the *background* or *setting* in which his characters live and act. We must ask ourselves certain questions about the setting. Is it in harmony with the people of the story? Or is it hostile to them? The setting can make a special contribution to the credibility of the story (make it more believable) and help to suggest the right atmosphere. Just how much or how little of a background is used can be important for seeing what the author is interested in. As readers we must study a story to find out what details of background the writer has chosen to present and what effect he wants them to have on his characters as well as on us.

SPEECH, DIALOGUE

The fourth element in a short story is *speech* (or *direct speech*) – that is, the actual words spoken by people. It is possible to tell a story without introducing direct speech, but generally a story is more convincing when characters are made to behave in this everyday way. Direct speech has a number of uses. It relieves pure narrative. It reveals character through showing thought. It points up something specially important. It indicates the social class or region or country from which somebody comes. It reveals how far a character is, for example, educated or clever.

THEME

In most short stories there is a *theme*. We must not confuse story and theme. The story is the succession of events put into a certain pattern. The theme is the lesson, or comment, or revelation or statement about some aspect of living contained in the sequence of events.

METHOD OF NARRATION

Even when an author has a story and characters in his mind, he still has to settle an important matter of technique – what is the best way in which to communicate these to his readers, *how to tell his story*. Every story has to be told from a certain *point of view* and the skilful writer will choose the point of view most suitable for his story. At one extreme he may choose to tell the story in the *first person* (*I, me, my, mine*) as if all the people and events were before his eyes as he tells us what he sees, hears, feels and thinks in a monologue. At the other end of the scale is the author as a kind of god, looking down from afar, seeing everything, knowing everything, understanding everything and choosing to tell whatever he wants to tell, all in the *third person* (*He, him, his, they, them, their, theirs*). Whatever the method of narration adopted, we can study it to learn how successful the writer has been in his choice and in his execution.

LANGUAGE

Most people who write are faced with the problem of finding the language that will best communicate what they have to say. So the short story writer has to decide on a kind of language that will be appropriate to the writing situation. It should be fitting for the narrator, for the characters and for the kind of story being told. Thus we may examine a short story to see the kind of vocabulary selected, the kinds of grammatical structures used, the other tricks or devices employed. Also, we must ask ourselves why these have been used and how successful the author has been in using them. Through his use of language, too, he may convey a certain *tone*: he may be, for example, critical, flippant, angry, childlike, naïve or haughty. And the tone he uses will affect the reader's attitude to the people and events in the story.

STRUCTURE

Finally, we may want to look at the over-all structure or shape of the story to see how our minds have been conditioned to the experience the author has to give.

Commentary: A Message from the Pig-Man

Character. In this story John Wain decides to work with a very small cast of characters. A small cast fits the small world he is dealing with. There are only four people, the main one being Eric, a little boy of six. Eric is presented partly as a child with specific problems in a specific situation, but also as a child with certain features that belong to any normal child of his age. He wants to appear grown-up. He has irrational fears. He has difficulty in understanding the adult world. His view of human relationships is a simple one. He loves playing with toys. He has a vivid imagination. By the time the story ends we know a great deal about Eric.

The other three people who are introduced into the story are left as sketchy characters: the mother, Donald, and the pig-man. They are not given any special qualities of personality – for example, the mother is just 'a mother'. They are merely used to reveal the tensions and problems faced by Eric. The social range is narrow: the household is vaguely lower-middle class and the pig-man, an alien figure intruding from another world, is working class. At the end of the story Eric is, in one respect, a different kind of person, for he has overcome his terror of the pig-man. He has learned one way of trying to solve problems in life. In another way, however, he is still the same, a little boy who is still left unsatisfied by adult attitudes.

Action, plot and incident. The author chooses a small domestic world, but an abnormal one. Within this world, all the events fit into the life of the child, Eric. Eric has two particular problems. He feels uncomfortable because for some reason his father is not living in the family home along with his mother and Donald. Another problem is that he doesn't know exactly what a pig-man is. He has a mental picture that terrifies him, and he is reluctant to ask anybody in the house to enlighten him.

The whole action of the story takes place on two separate days. The opening situation, presented through Eric's thoughts, reveals a critical stage in the boy's life and the events that have made it critical. His father has gone, replaced at home and in his mother's affections by another man, Donald. Eric wants his father back to make a household of four. His mother had asked him to take things to the pig bin and he was terrified of the next step he might be asked to take. The two problems are united in Eric's frightened mind.

The complications are the more effective because of the warm calm atmosphere of the dining-room in which he plays with that most harmless of familiar things, his train set. At each successive step in events Eric becomes more terrified, feels more like a victim.

The writer deals very cleverly with the crisis. First he leads up to the meeting with the pig-man and in a false crisis, makes Eric escape the meeting. This delays the crisis and his mother's command brings the meeting about. But just as there were two problems for Eric so there are two crises – a very clever touch by the author. The new insight into the nature of life provided by the meeting with the pig-man is used by the author to lead Eric to attempt to solve the other problem of his father's absence, but unsuccessfully.

Thus there are also two dénouements. One is that Eric has learned an important lesson on how to tackle problems in life. The other is that not all problems are capable of such a solution. He is left angry at the imperfections of the adults and the adult world. He is still 'Poor little Ekky' and hates 'them all, all, *all*'.

It is noticeable that almost all of the separate actions and events are commonplace but that their arrangement gives them a greater significance because they are woven into the life of a little human being to whom they are not commonplace.

Background and setting. Although the setting is of less importance than the personality of Eric or the events that happen to him, nevertheless

John Wain is careful to make his background fit the life of the central character. The setting is small and limited, and this befits a child's world. It consists of a house, a backyard and a bit of a street. Each part of the background suggests something different: comfort, love in the house; danger and discomfort in the backyard with its pig bin; terror in the street with the pig-man's pail. Naturally, most attention is paid to the domestic interior, and it is interesting to notice the kind of items used by the author to create a suitable background for the six-year-old boy – his bed, the spare room, egg shells and tea leaves, a dining-room and a train set, a baking bowl and a brown paper carrier bag. There is no detailed description of any single item of the setting, yet by the artful use of little details the author provides a framework that we can believe in. Just because he puts little emphasis on it, our attention is kept on Eric and his problems. It serves to heighten the human feelings. It helps to give us, by its ordinariness, a sense that life can be more mysterious than we are accustomed to think, and that in humdrum backgrounds there may lurk human tensions we don't readily see.

Speech and dialogue. For most of the story the author uses direct speech very sparingly. Only the mother's words are given and only the words she speaks in connection with the pig-man, thus emphasizing one of the two central interests of the story. It is in the latter half of the story that dialogue occurs. There it is used to give extra vitality and human feeling to the two crises in the story, the meeting with the pig-man and the question of Eric's father's return to the household. But speech is also used as a means of revealing social class. Eric, his mother and Donald all use 'correct' English with normal pronunciation and with the kind of language that reveals a civilized attitude or behaviour: expressions such as 'dear', 'will you', 'Do be a good, sweet boy' or 'old man'. By contrast with such language we have the rather coarse dialect speech of the pig-man such as 'Arh, Aarh, Harh, Harh' and 'if that's whatcher mean'. The social status and lack of education of the pig-man is further emphasized by his use of abnormal grammatical forms such as 'they likes' or 'I leaves' or by minor sentences (sentences without a subject and predicate) such as 'the old porkers' and 'Only not fruit skins'.

Theme. You will notice that the title gives an indication of the theme – *A Message from the Pig-Man.* In the story the pig-man does not openly give a message at all. The message is deduced by Eric. The story is of a highly significant incident in a child's life. It might be said there are two interlocked themes. One is the child's problem of not understanding new expressions and the consequent fear that lack of understanding brings. The second is the child's difficulty in understanding the rules of the grown-up world. The themes are interlocked because the answer to one difficulty is used to try to solve the more important one.

The author gives signposts that keep the major theme in our minds while the story progresses. Such signposts are:

'Nothing will be changed.'

It was so hard to read the signs.

So that was how you did it. You just went straight ahead.

'That's a hard one.'

'Poor little Ekky.'

Grown-ups were mad and silly and he hated them all, all, *all.*

Narrative method. The author was obviously faced with a ticklish problem of how to make a child's thinking and actions genuinely interesting to adult readers. Part of his solution was by the method of narration or point of view of the teller of the story.

First of all, we should notice that John Wain makes himself a third-person anonymous narrator. He is content to tell the story without obtruding anything of his own view of events into it. Indeed, he chooses to tell his story almost wholly from the point of view of the central character, only occasionally stepping back from the boy's thoughts, actions and feelings. Everything that happens in the story happens while Eric is present. It is almost like a bit of disguised autobiography. The method may be illustrated like this:

Third person: He knew Donald, of course, and felt all right about his being in the house, though it seemed, when he lay in bed and thought about it, mad and pointless that Donald's coming should mean that Dad had to go.'

First person: 'I know Donald, of course, and feel all right about his being in the house, though it seems, when I lie in bed and think about it, mad and pointless that Donald's coming should mean Dad had to go.'

Notice the advantages of this particular kind of third-person narration. A lot of the text is of the reported speech kind, so that the reader can be involved in the workings of Eric's personal life; and yet the author is still free to guide the reader by adding facts or by using more adult language to sustain the story at a higher level than the child's thoughts.

Thus the author is able to give power and vitality and a kind of authenticity to his accurate observation of the working of a child's mind. He makes the reader see as significant and important what might otherwise be dismissed as a trivial little happening.

Language: First, the author tries to establish the sense of a child's mind operating from a child's world. The tone of the language is one of serious sympathy. He wants to suggest to the reader that most of the story is coming out of Eric's mind, so he has to use language that will make the child's speech and thought credible.

Notice some of the techniques employed for this purpose. There are many short sentences. Most of the longer sentences are made up of short clauses joined together by the simplest of connections, those used most frequently by children, such as *and, but, so.* There are many 'minor sentences' (sentences without subjects or predicates) which suggest a child's-eye view.

The childish habit of over-emphasizing words for effect is conveyed by italicizing words. This is carried further by italicizing whole sentences. By using italics the author makes us think the words are spoken loudly, but he also makes us understand that they are of vital importance in the story.

The vocabulary is kept very simple, much of it consisting of words that Eric would understand. Much of it is words he could say. Also, the language is peppered with little phrases that suggest how a child thinks: *real boy, the funny teeth, a bit nice, Dad* and *Mum*. There are a great number of questions inserted into the text: this suggests the childlike questing mind as well as the genuine bewilderment of Eric. Except in the momentous meeting with the pig-man, the language is plain and straightforward.

During the account of the meeting we get the drama heightened by the use of simile and metaphor:

Similes

It was the same as getting into icy-cold water.

His heart was banging like fireworks going off.

Metaphor

Everything, even his fear, sank and drowned in the raging tide of his curiosity. Notice how the images used are appropriate to the kind of experiences a young, well-off, middle-class boy could have had: *icy-cold water, fireworks, the sea.*

Structure: The shape of the story is quite simple. The story is in two parts, each of them occupying part of a day, and each part linked by a very brief paragraph of six lines ('Still there was school . . . came to a crisis'). In the first part, the author tries to establish the character or personality of Eric and his particular fears and bewilderments. In the second, he concentrates on the solution of the problems in two episodes, one with the pig-man and one back home with his mother and Donald.

Projections – 1

1. Here is a piece of first-person narrative. Turn it into third-person narrative:
   'I strain my eyes, peering into the half darkness. I am not sure if the movement is that of some wild animal. Fear grips my throat. The light is bad and makes it difficult to sort out some distinct shape. I hear a sudden ominous rustling. Maybe it is only a rabbit.'
2. Look carefully at the kind of language used by the pig-man, then try writing a short piece of direct speech in which he tells of his meeting with Eric.
3. Imagine that Eric overhears the discussion that his father, his mother and Donald have about settling their affairs before the father leaves.

Script the discussion. You could write it as a short play or as a short story.

4. Eric's mother, in a letter to her husband, tells the story from the point at which she asks Eric to take the brown carrier to the pig bin.
5. 'Nothing will be changed', Eric had been promised. Look at the initial situation and the remainder of the story and try to decide if this is true. (You could discuss this in a group, and record the different opinions expressed.)
6. Which aspect of the storyteller's art strikes you as most skilfully handled by John Wain in this story? Study the features described in STUDY AIDS – 1 and support your choice with details from the story.

First Confession
by Frank O'Connor

All the trouble began when my grandfather died and my grandmother – my father's mother – came to live with us. Relations in the one house are a strain at the best of times, but, to make matters worse, my grandmother was a real old countrywoman and quite unsuited to the life in town. She had a fat, wrinkled old face, and, to Mother's great indignation, went round the house in bare feet –

the boots had her crippled, she said. For dinner she had a jug of porter and a pot of potatoes with – sometimes – a bit of salt fish, and she poured out the potatoes on the table and ate them slowly, with great relish, using her fingers by way of a fork.

Now, girls are supposed to be fastidious, but I was the one who suffered most from this. Nora, my sister, just sucked up to the old woman for the penny she got every Friday out of the old-age pension, a thing I could not do. I was too honest, that was my trouble; and when I was playing with Bill Connell, the sergeant major's son, and saw my grandmother steering up the path with the jug of porter sticking out from beneath her shawl I was mortified. I made excuses not to let him come into the house, because I could never be sure what she would be up to when we went in.

When Mother was at work and my grandmother made the dinner I wouldn't touch it. Nora once tried to make me, but I hid under the table from her and took the bread knife with me for protection. Nora let on to be very indignant (she wasn't, of course, but she knew Mother saw through her, so she sided with Gran) and came after me. I lashed out at her with the bread knife, and after that she left me alone. I stayed there till Mother came in from work and made my dinner, but when Father came in later Nora said in a shocked voice: 'Oh, Dadda, do you know what Jackie did at dinnertime?' Then, of course, it all came out; Father gave me a flaking; Mother interfered, and for days after that he didn't speak to me and Mother barely spoke to Nora. And all because of that old woman! God knows, I was heart-scalded.

Then, to crown my misfortunes, I had to make my first confession and communion. It was an old woman called Ryan who prepared us for these. She was about the one age with Gran; she was well-to-do, lived in a big house on Montenotte, wore a black cloak and bonnet, and came every day to school at three o'clock when we should have been going home, and talked to us of hell. She may have mentioned the other place as well, but that could only have been by accident, for hell had the first place in her heart.

She lit a candle, took out a new half crown, and offered it to the first boy who would hold one finger – only one finger! – in the flame for five minutes by the school clock. Being always very ambitious I was tempted to volunteer, but I thought it might look greedy. Then she asked were we afraid of holding one finger – only one finger! – in a little candle flame for five minutes and not afraid of burning all over in roasting hot furnaces for all eternity. 'All eternity! Just

think of that! A whole lifetime goes by and it's nothing, not even a drop in the ocean of your sufferings.' The woman was really interesting about hell, but my attention was all fixed on the half crown. At the end of the lesson she put it back in her purse. It was a great disappointment; a religious woman like that, you wouldn't think she'd bother about a thing like a half crown.

Another day she said she knew a priest who woke one night to find a fellow he didn't recognize leaning over the end of his bed. The priest was a bit frightened – naturally enough – but he asked the fellow what he wanted, and the fellow said in a deep, husky voice that he wanted to go to confession. The priest said it was an awkward time and wouldn't it do in the morning, but the fellow said that last time he went to confession, there was one sin he kept back, being ashamed to mention it, and now it was always on his mind. Then the priest knew it was a bad case, because the fellow was after making a bad confession and committing a mortal sin. He got up to dress, and just then the cock crew in the yard outside, and – lo and behold! – when the priest looked round there was no sign of the fellow, only a smell of burning timber, and when the priest looked at his bed didn't he see the print of two hands burned in it? That was because the fellow had made a bad confession. This story made a shocking impression on me.

But the worst of all was when she showed us how to examine our conscience. Did we take the name of the Lord, our God, in vain? Did we honour our father and our mother? (I asked her did this include grandmothers and she said it did.) Did we love our neighbours as ourselves? Did we covet our neighbour's goods? (I thought of the way I felt about the penny that Nora got every Friday.) I decided that, between one thing and another, I must have broken the whole ten commandments, all on account of that old woman, and so far as I could see, so long as she remained in the house I had no hope of ever doing anything else.

I was scared to death of confession. The day the whole class went I let on to have a toothache, hoping my absence wouldn't be noticed; but at three o'clock, just as I was feeling safe, along comes a chap with a message from Mrs. Ryan that I was to go to confession myself on Saturday and be at the chapel for communion with the rest. To make it worse, Mother couldn't come with me and sent Nora instead.

Now, that girl had ways of tormenting me that Mother never knew of. She held my hand as we went down the hill, smiling sadly and saying how sorry she was for me, as if she were bringing me to the hospital for an operation.

'Oh, God help us!' she moaned. 'Isn't it a terrible pity you weren't a good boy? Oh, Jackie, my heart bleeds for you! How will you ever think of all your sins? Don't forget you have to tell him about the time you kicked Gran on the shin.'

'Lemme go!' I said, trying to drag myself free of her. 'I don't want to go to confession at all.'

'But sure, you'll have to go to confession, Jackie,' she replied in the same regretful tone. 'Sure, if you didn't, the parish priest would be up to the house, looking for you. 'Tisn't, God knows, that I'm not sorry for you. Do you remember the time you tried to kill me with the bread knife under the table? And the language you used to me? I don't know what he'll do with you at all, Jackie. He might have to send you up to the bishop.'

I remember thinking bitterly that she didn't know the half of what I had to tell – if I told it. I knew I couldn't tell it, and understood perfectly why the fellow in Mrs. Ryan's story made a bad confession; it seemed to me a great shame that people wouldn't stop criticizing him. I remember that steep hill down to the church, and the sunlit hillsides beyond the valley of the river, which I saw in the gaps between the houses like Adam's last glimpse of Paradise.

Then, when she had manoeuvred me down the long flight of steps to the chapel yard, Nora suddenly changed her tone. She became the raging malicious devil she really was.

'There you are!' she said with a yelp of triumph, hurling me through the church door. 'And I hope he'll give you the penitential psalms, you dirty little caffler.'

I knew then I was lost, given up to eternal justice. The door with the coloured glass panels swung shut behind me, the sunlight went out and gave place to deep shadow, and the wind whistled outside so that the silence within seemed to crackle like ice under my feet. Nora sat in front of me by the confession box. There were a couple of old women ahead of her, and then a miserable-looking poor devil came and wedged me in at the other side, so that I couldn't escape even if I had the courage. He joined his hands and rolled his eyes in the direction of the roof, muttering aspirations in an anguished tone, and I wondered had he a grandmother too. Only a grandmother could account for a fellow behaving in that heartbroken way, but he was better off than I, for he at least could go and confess his sins; while I would make a bad confession and then die in the night and be continually coming back and burning people's furniture.

Nora's turn came, and I heard the sound of something slamming, and then her voice as if butter wouldn't melt in her mouth, and then another slam, and out she came. God, the hypocrisy of women. Her eyes were lowered, her head was bowed, and her hands were joined very low down on her stomach, and she walked up the aisle to the side altar looking like a saint. You never saw such an exhibition of devotion; and I remembered the devilish malice with which she had tormented me all the way from our door, and wondered were all religious people like that, really. It was my turn now. With the fear of damnation in my soul I went in, and the confessional door closed of itself behind me.

It was pitch dark and I couldn't see the priest or anything else. Then I really began to be frightened. In the darkness it was a matter between God and me, and He had all the odds. He knew what my intentions were before I even started; I had no chance. All I had ever been told about confession got mixed up in my mind, and I knelt to one wall and said: 'Bless me, father, for I have sinned; this is my first confession.' I waited for a few minutes, but nothing happened, so I tried it on the other wall. Nothing happened there either. He had me spotted all right.

It must have been then that I noticed the shelf at about one height with my head. It was really a place for grown-up people to rest their elbows, but in my distracted state I thought it was probably the place you were supposed to kneel. Of course, it was on the high side and not very deep, but I was always good at climbing and managed to get up all right. Staying up was the trouble. There was room only for my knees, and nothing you could get a grip on but a sort of wooden moulding a bit above it. I held on to the moulding and repeated the words a little louder, and this time something happened all right. A slide was slammed back; a little light entered the box, and a man's voice said: 'Who's there?'

''Tis me, father,' I said for fear he mightn't see me and go away again. I couldn't see him at all. The place the voice came from was under the moulding, about level with my knees, so I took a good grip of the moulding and swung myself down till I saw the astonished face of a young priest looking up at me. He had to put his head on one side to see me, and I had to put mine on one side to see him, so we were more or less talking to one another upside-down. It struck me as a queer way of hearing confessions, but I didn't feel it my place to criticize.

'Bless me, father, for I have sinned; this is my first confession,' I rattled off all in one breath, and swung myself down the least shade more to make it easier for him.

'What are you doing up there?' he shouted in an angry voice, and the strain the politeness was putting on my hold of the moulding, and the shock of being addressed in such an uncivil tone, were too much for me. I lost my grip, tumbled, and hit the door an unmerciful wallop before I found myself flat on my back in the middle of the aisle. The people who had been waiting stood up with their mouths open. The priest opened the door of the middle box and came out, pushing his biretta back from his forehead; he looked something terrible. Then Nora came scampering down the aisle.

'Oh, you dirty little caffler!' she said. 'I might have known you'd do it. I might have known you'd disgrace me. I can't leave you out of my sight for onc minute.'

Before I could even get to my feet to defend myself she bent down and gave me a clip across the ear. This reminded me that I was so stunned I had even forgotten to cry, so that people might think I wasn't hurt at all, when in fact I was probably maimed for life. I gave a roar out of me.

'What's all this about?' the priest hissed, getting angrier than ever and pushing Nora off me. 'How dare you hit the child like that, you little vixen?'

'But I can't do my penance with him, father,' Nora cried, cocking an outraged eye up at him.

'Well, go and do it, or I'll give you some more to do,' he said, giving me a hand up. 'Was it coming to confession you were, my poor man?' he asked me.

''Twas, father,' said I with a sob.

'Oh,' he said respectfully, 'a big hefty fellow like you must have terrible sins. Is this your first?'

''Tis, father,' said I.

'Worse and worse,' he said gloomily. 'The crimes of a lifetime. I don't know will I get rid of you at all today. You'd better wait now till I'm finished with these old ones. You can see by the looks of them they haven't much to tell.'

'I will, father,' I said with something approaching joy.

The relief of it was really enormous. Nora stuck out her tongue at me from behind his back, but I couldn't even be bothered retorting. I knew from the very moment that man opened his mouth that he was intelligent above the ordinary. When I had time to think,

I saw how right I was. It only stood to reason that a fellow confessing after seven years would have more to tell than people that went every week. The crimes of a lifetime, exactly as he said. It was only what he expected, and the rest was the cackle of old women and girls with their talk of hell, the bishop, and the penitential psalms. That was all they knew. I started to make my examination of conscience, and barring the one bad business of my grandmother it didn't seem so bad.

The next time, the priest steered me into the confession box himself and left the shutter back the way I could see him get in and sit down at the further side of the grille from me.

'Well, now,' he said, 'what do they call you?'

'Jackie, father,' said I.

'And what's a-trouble to you, Jackie?'

'Father,' I said, feeling I might as well get it over while I had him in good humour, 'I had it all arranged to kill my grandmother.'

He seemed a bit shaken by that, all right, because he said nothing for quite a while.

'My goodness,' he said at last, 'that'd be a shocking thing to do. What put that into your head?'

'Father,' I said, feeling very sorry for myself, 'she's an awful woman.'

'Is she?' he asked. 'What way is she awful?'

'She takes porter, father.' I said, knowing well from the way Mother talked of it that this was a mortal sin, and hoping it would make the priest take a more favourable view of my case.

'Oh, my!' he said, and I could see he was impressed.

'And snuff, father,' said I.

'That's a bad case, sure enough, Jackie,' he said.

'And she goes round in her bare feet, father,' I went on in a rush of self-pity, 'and she knows I don't like her, and she gives pennies to Nora and none to me, and my dad sides with her and flakes me, and one night I was so heart-scalded I made up my mind I'd have to kill her.'

'And what would you do with the body?' he asked with great interest.

'I was thinking I could chop that up and carry it away in a barrow I have,' I said.

'Begor, Jackie,' he said, 'do you know you're a terrible child?'

'I know, father,' I said, for I was just thinking the same thing myself. 'I tried to kill Nora too with a bread knife under the table, only I missed her.'

'Is that the little girl that was beating you just now?' he asked.

''Tis, father.'

'Someone will go for her with a bread knife one day, and he won't miss her,' he said rather cryptically. 'You must have great courage. Between ourselves, there's a lot of people I'd like to do the same to but I'd never have the nerve. Hanging is an awful death.'

'Is it, father?' I asked with the deeper interest – I was always very keen on hanging. 'Did you ever see a fellow hanged?'

'Dozens of them,' he said solemnly. 'And they all died roaring.'

'Jay!' I said.

'Oh, a horrible death!' he said with great satisfaction. 'Lots of the fellows I saw killed their grandmothers too, but they all said 'twas never worth it.'

He had me there for a full ten minutes talking, and then walked out the chapel yard with me. I was genuinely sorry to part with him, because he was the most entertaining character I'd ever met in the religious line. Outside, after the shadow of the church, the sunlight was like the roaring of waves on a beach; it dazzled me; and when the frozen silence melted and I heard the screech of trams on the road my heart soared. I knew now I wouldn't die in the night and come back, leaving marks on my mother's furniture. It would be a great worry to her, and the poor soul had enough.

Nora was sitting on the railing, waiting for me, and she put on a very sour puss when she saw the priest with me. She was mad jealous because a priest had never come out of the church with her.

'Well,' she asked coldly, after he left me, 'what did he give you?'

'Three Hail Marys,' I said.

'Three Hail Marys,' she repeated incredulously. 'You mustn't have told him anything.'

'I told him everything,' I said confidently.

'About Gran and all?'

'About Gran and all.'

(All she wanted was to be able to go home and say I'd made a bad confession.)

'Did you tell him you went for me with the bread knife?' she asked with a frown.

'I did to be sure.'

'And he only gave you three Hail Marys?'

'That's all.'

She slowly got down from the railing with a baffled air. Clearly, this was beyond her. As we mounted the steps back to the main road she looked at me suspiciously.

'What are you sucking?' she asked.

'Bullseyes.'

'Was it the priest gave them to you?'

''Twas.'

'Lord God,' she wailed bitterly, 'some people have all the luck! 'Tis no advantage to anybody trying to be good. I might just as well be a sinner like you.'

Reading Aids – 2

page 28: *first confession* an important landmark in the religious life of the Roman Catholic when for the first time he tells the priest of sins committed so as to obtain absolution and punishment.

29 *porter* a dark brown beer.

fastidious fussy about manners, etc.

sucked up to wormed her way into friendship by flattery or cajolery.

the sergeant major the man in charge of the local Territorial Army unit.

mortified severely vexed, humiliated or ashamed.

flaking beating.

heart-scalded his feelings were hurt.

the one age with Gran the same age as Gran.

communion Holy Communion or Mass – a ceremony with bread and wine commemorating the Last Supper.

31 *a mortal sin* a sin that, unless repented of and forgiven, will cause eternal death and damnation.

made a bad confession did not tell the whole truth.

ten commandments the laws given through Moses to the children of Israel.

32 *send you up to the Bishop* for an extraordinarily serious sin.

Adam's last glimpse of Paradise the last look Adam had of his former dwelling place, Eden or Paradise, when God expelled him for the sin of eating the apple from the tree of knowledge. This is appropriate here as Jackie is leaving the bright carefree child's world for a new situation in which he will constantly have to take account of sin.

manoeuvred pushed and pulled; drove.

penitential psalms Numbers 6, 32, 38, 51, 102, 130 and 143 – a terrifying task for a little boy of seven.

caffler nuisance.

confession box a stall in which the priest and penitent sit with a partition separating them.

aspirations hopes; wishes.
anguished pained.
33 *hypocrisy* pretending to be what you are not.
aisle passage between rows of pews in a church.
malice ill-will.
he had all the odds everything was in his favour.
35 *biretta* special hat of particular shape worn by the clergy of the Roman Catholic Church: red for Cardinals, purple for Bishops, black for priests.
36 *grille* openwork screen through which priest and penitent communicate in the confessional.
37 *cryptically* with an underlying meaning.
Hanging is an awful death 'hanging by the neck' was then punishment for the convicted murderer.
Jay! for J(esus).
Hail Marys name of a prayer of invocation to the blessed Virgin Mary: given as a penance.
38 *bullseyes* black-and-white striped peppermint balls.

Study Aids – 2

Commentary: First Confession

Character. The central character, Jackie, is a little boy seven years old and the central happening is his first confession. Jackie is not portrayed as an active instigator of events, except in the actual confession. He is someone who is acted on; and this is true to life. All the other characters are directly concerned with Jackie's state of sin.

The characters are fairly well developed for a short story, so that we form quite clear pictures of the grandmother, of Nora, of Mrs Ryan, and of the priest. We get some feeling of their personalities. But all the characters are presented because of the particular function they have in Jackie's preparation for his first communion. Thus the grandmother is a *source* of sin as well as of particular *acts* of sin. Nora is a constant irritant. Mrs Ryan elaborates on the punishments that await the sinner who makes a 'bad confession', and the priest hears the first confession and deals with the terrible sinner. The first three are flawed human beings, but the priest is presented as a kind of ideal father-confessor, who can see – behind the ugly façade people present – the real heart of the matter.

For a short story, the range of characters presented is wide, from the rich middle class of city society to the poverty-formed old grandmother. There is also a wide range of ages, from the child to the very old. A good short story is made up of very different characters in action, but here each one is shown as seriously affecting Jackie, either in his outer life or the inner life of the imagination and feelings.

But it is Jackie's character which is most fully developed. We see him as serious, anxious to make a good impression, honest, naíve, fastidious, sensitive about the ridicule his grandmother may bring him, ambitious, with a vivid imagination. It is odd, but effective, that Jackie is left as a loner in the story, that neither father nor mother is developed as a character. All the main characters (except the priest) are given a name, so that we get an added sense of reality as we accept them in the same way as we accept named people in our everyday lives.

An additional character, of course, is the narrator himself. It is obvious, although he does not anywhere give a clue as to his age at the time of telling, that he is a mature man and that very many years separate him from the boy of seven. Thus, by the things he says about the far-off incident and people, by the kind of language he uses, we feel that he is a well-educated, calm, rather philosophic man, and the story gains in credibility because of these qualities of character that come through in the telling of the story.

Action, plot and incident. Frank O'Connor emphasizes incident as much as character. Although all the incidents are chosen for the effect they have upon Jackie, there is an astonishing variety of them. They range from the eating of potatoes off the table and slashing at the sister with the bread knife to tumbling out of a confessional box and eating sweets given by a priest at first confession. The happenings are individually vivid and unusual, and put together they make a story in which one action follows another in rapid succession. But if some of the incidents are unusual they are also perfectly credible. We accept them as things that could happen in real life. We should notice that the author has selected incidents from a fairly long period of time: the duration of the total action is left vague. But the very vagueness helps to create the feeling that the boy is being pressured and pressured, and that he is accumulating sins for which he is to be called to account.

The initial situation is cleverly disguised by incident, but it is in reality describing the state of sinfulness that the boy feels himself to be in. This state of sinfulness is complicated by the teaching of Mrs Ryan, by Nora's baiting, by the man waiting for confession and by the blunders of Jackie's first attempt, certainly a 'bad confession'. The crisis is, of course, the 'good confession' in which his fears are proved groundless.

The dénouement is a new kind of awareness about this aspect of religious life and a new phase in his relationship with his tormentor, Nora. We should also note that Frank O'Connor has a keen sense of the ridiculous and contrives hilarious and grotesque actions in the confessional box. His sense of humour tends towards the farcical.

Background and setting. The author is much more concerned with people and what they do than with the setting in which his characters act.

He does not give us any elaborate descriptions of the home or the school or the church. That is not to say that he does not have objects that form a kind of background. He uses significant details to point up character or heighten the action; for example, the potatoes on the table, the bread knife, the half crown, the candle, the moulding in the confessional box and the bulls-eyes. It would seem that the author feels that precise pictures of places and their contents would detract from the power of characters and actions.

But there are two rather special uses of background detail. In both cases natural phenomena are used. The first occurs when Nora hurls Jackie through the door of the church and he himself feels he is a lamb given over to the slaughter. The author writes: 'the sunlight went out and gave place to deep shadow, and the wind whistled outside so that the silence seemed to crackle like ice under my feet.' Again, in contrast, when he emerges, having shriven his soul: 'the sunlight was like the roaring of waves on a beach; it dazzled me; and when the frozen silence melted . . .' This use of nature to reflect a human being's state of mind is sometimes called 'the pathetic fallacy' – but it is a clever way of emphasizing a character's mental condition.

Speech and dialogue. We can notice two main uses of direct speech in this story. First of all, it is employed to relieve the monotony of the narrative and at the same time to indicate something of importance in Jackie's life. Thus his sister tells his father of the bread knife incident in direct speech, Mrs Ryan tells of the torments of hell for all eternity, and Jackie, in an amusing first attempt at confession, speaks to the wooden walls of the confession box.

Secondly, it is used to give us a more vivid picture of the relations and the feelings of the characters, including their comic side. For example, language is used to show Nora's viciousness when taking Jackie to church. It is used to show the skilfulness of the priest in handling the boy's fears. And it is used to show Jackie's triumph over a bewildered Nora. Nora uses direct speech to reveal the final meaning behind all the events and the fairy tale ending of the bad being punished and the good rewarded. Direct speech is also used to indicate age – for example, with Nora's 'Dadda . . .' It is used to show social status – for example, the almost pure English of Mrs Ryan. It also shows nationality, as with the Irish vocabulary in the speech of Nora and Jackie. We can notice, too, how direct speech is handled in the final episode with Nora and Jackie: short phrases are used, with repetition, to convey disbelief on the one hand and triumph on the other, until Nora's important closing words.

Theme: The central theme is another of the problems of childhood, in this case one special to children of the Roman Catholic faith – the importance of making a good first confession. Behind the narrative lie other suggestions: that it is impossible for the layman to recognize the real nature of sin; that knowing what is right and what is wrong is a problem. The answer is put in Nora's mouth: ''Tis no advantage to anybody trying to be good. I might just as well be a sinner like you.' Throughout the story Frank O'Connor keeps reminding us of the theme. 'I had to make my first confession and communion'; 'I was scared to death of confession'; 'I had no chance'; 'The relief of it was really enormous'.

Narrative method. The unique flavour of the story arises largely from the first-person narrative method employed. This fixes the point of view from which events are told. Frank O'Connor chooses to tell it as if he were a much much older version of the boy who had all the experiences described. But these experiences have merely served as the raw materials. From these the writer has selected a pattern of events and gives them a particular shape. There is a difference between the sometimes painful nature of the actual experiences and the point of view taken by the older narrator. The latter, with the lapse of age, sees the whole business as being very funny, but with serious undertones. He refines the raw material by observation, deduction and thoughtful comment. Thus there is always a contrast between the child that was and the man that is, the wise narrator. The author is able to tap the springs of laughter by constantly pointing out the difference between what *seems* and what really *is*.

Language. One of the first requirements of the writer is that he should give the impression of actually speaking. To achieve this he adopts various devices of speech and fits them into his prose.

We should notice that he is very restrained in the use of 'I', and this restraint gives a sense of distance and calmness.

To make the dialogue realistic he uses colloquial forms, such as *wouldn't*, and *couldn't*. Another trick that lends realism is the dash for parenthesis or for that little extra bit of information just recalled. Others are the aside, the exclamation mark and the question mark.

The narrator's vocabulary shows him to be an educated Irishman. As such, he introduces Irish words into the story and allows himself an extensive vocabulary, but never so much as to upset the realistic quality of the story. This skilful mixture of Irish with educated English allows him to deal convincingly with the two worlds, that of the adult writer and of the seven-year-old boy.

The general tone is one of pleasant intimacy, tinged with humour: he sees the little oddities of thought and behaviour as well as the gross absurdities of situations. Since the narrator is mature, he can tell his story in a full range of sentence structures. He makes effective use of short sentences, especially at key points in the story. Even when using the long and involved sentence he manages to convey a conversational flavour.

Structure. As in *On Saturday Afternoon* the author takes great care to establish the character of the main figure at the beginning, along with the problem that constitutes the theme of the story. After that, all the incidents are relevant to that theme. The most elaborate episode is reserved for the actual confession itself. As the story proceeds, more and more dialogue is introduced. This increase tends to stress the human difficulties of the boy's situation.

Projections – 2

1. Jackie's grandmother makes his life a misery. Think of someone (or invent someone) whose presence and actions make your life a misery. Write a brief account of him or her. Try using as bitter and cruel words as you can. If you like, you could use Jackie's account as a model, perhaps changing his words into words used in your own neighbourhood.
2. Write a first-person account of a past experience. Try to create the feeling that you are speaking in everyday language. Use the characteristic marks of speech: the use of 'I' and 'me', the parenthesis, italicized words, the question and exclamation.
3. You know Nora's character and her attitude to Jackie. Invent the bad-tempered account she gives to her grandmother of the events of the confession. You could write this as a play or a short story.
4. Imagine a newspaper reporter has got wind of the confession incident of Jackie's falling into the aisle. He interviews both Jackie and Nora and pieces together a report for his paper. Write the report. Use an appropriate headline. You could study a real newspaper article to help you get some idea of the way they use sentences.
5. Frank O'Connor has attempted a humorous story. Make a list of the funny things Jackie says and thinks. What makes them funny, in your opinion? Choose what you think is the funniest incident. Try to explain its comicality.
6. 'The most entertaining character I'd ever met in the religious line' is Jackie's description of the priest. In what way do you think of him as entertaining and in what way was he much more than just entertaining?

On Saturday Afternoon

by Alan Sillitoe

I once saw a bloke try to kill himself. I'll never forget the day because I was sitting in the house one Saturday afternoon, feeling black and fed up because everybody in the family had gone to the pictures, except me who'd for some reason been left out of it. 'Course, I didn't know then that I would soon see something you can never see in the same way on the pictures, a real bloke stringing himself up. I was only a kid at the time, so you can imagine how much I enjoyed it.

I've never known a family to look as black as our family when they're fed up. I've seen the old man with his face so dark and full of murder because he ain't got no fags or was having to use saccharine to sweeten his tea, or even for nothing at all, that I've backed out of the house in case he got up from his fireside chair and came for me. He just sits, almost on top of the fire, his oil-stained Sunday-joint maulers opened out in front of him and facing inwards to each other, his thick shoulders scrunched forward, and his dark brown eyes staring into the fire. Now and again he'd say a dirty word, for no reason at all, the worst word you can think of, and when he starts saying this you know it's time to clear out. If mam's in it gets worse than ever, because she says sharp to him: 'What are yo' looking so bleddy black for?' as if it might be because of something she's done, and before you know what's happening he's tipped up a tableful of pots and mam's gone out of the house crying. Dad hunches back over the fire and goes on swearing. All because of a packet of fags.

I once saw him broodier than I'd ever seen him, so that I thought he'd gone crackers in a quiet sort of way – until a fly flew to within a yard of him. Then his hand shot out, got it, and slung it crippled into the roaring fire. After that he cheered up a bit and mashed some tea.

Well, that's where the rest of us get our black looks from. It stands to reason we'd have them with a dad who carries on like that, don't it? Black looks run in the family. Some families have them and some don't. Our family has them right enough, and that's certain, so when we're fed up we're really fed up. Nobody knows why we get as fed up as we do or why it gives us these black looks when we are. Some people get fed up and don't look bad at all: they seem happy in a funny sort of way, as if they've just been set free from clink after being in there for something they didn't do, or come out of the pictures after sitting plugged for eight hours at a bad film, or just missed a bus they ran half a mile for and seen it was the wrong one just after they'd stopped running – but in our family it's murder for the others if one of us is fed up. I've asked myself lots of times what it is, but I can never get any sort of answer even if I sit and think for hours, which I must admit I don't do, though it looks good when I say I do. But I sit and think for long enough, until mam says to me, at seeing me scrunched up over the fire like dad: 'What are yo' looking so black for?' So I've just got to stop thinking about it in case I get really black and fed up and go the same way as dad, tipping up a tableful of pots and all.

Mostly I suppose there's nothing to look so black for: though it's nobody's fault and you can't blame anyone for looking black because I'm sure it's summat in the blood. But on this Saturday afternoon I was looking so black that when dad came in from the bookie's he said to me: 'What's up wi' yo'?'

'I feel badly,' I fibbed. He'd have had a fit if I'd said I was only black because I hadn't gone to the pictures.

'Well have a wash,' he told me.

'I don't want a wash,' I said, and that was a fact.

'Well, get outside and get some fresh air then,' he shouted.

I did as I was told, double quick, because if ever dad goes as far as to tell me to get some fresh air I know it's time to get away from him. But outside the air wasn't so fresh, what with that bloody great bike factory bashing away at the yard-end. I didn't know where to go, so I walked up the yard a bit and sat down near somebody's back gate.

Then I saw this bloke who hadn't lived long in our yard. He was tall and thin and had a face like a parson except that he wore a flat cap and had a moustache that drooped, and looked as though he hadn't had a square meal for a year. I didn't think much o' this at the time: but I remember that as he turned in by the yard-end one of the nosy gossiping women who stood there every minute of the day except when she trudged to the pawnshop with her husband's bike or best suit, shouted to him: 'What's that rope for, mate?'

He called back: 'It's to 'ang messen wi', missis,' and she cackled at his bloody good joke so loud and long you'd think she never heard such a good 'un, though the next day she cackled on the other side of her fat face.

He walked by me puffing a fag and carrying his coil of brand-new rope, and he had to step over me to get past. His boot nearly took my shoulder off, and when I told him to watch where he was going I don't think he heard me because he didn't even look round. Hardly anybody was about. All the kids were still at the pictures, and most of their mams and dads were downtown doing the shopping.

The bloke walked down the yard to his back door, and having nothing better to do because I hadn't gone to the pictures I followed him. You see, he left his back door open a bit, so I gave it a push and went in. I stood there, just watching him, sucking my thumb, the other hand in my pocket. I suppose he knew I was there, because his eyes were moving more natural now, but he didn't seem to mind. 'What are yer going to do wi' that rope, mate?' I asked him.

'I'm going ter 'ang messen, lad,' he told me as though he'd done it a time or two already, and people had usually asked him questions like this beforehand.

'What for, mate?' He must have thought I was a nosy young bogger.

''Cause I want to, that's what for,' he said, clearing all the pots off the table and pulling it to the middle of the room. Then he stood on it to fasten the rope to the light fitting. The table creaked and didn't look very safe, but it did him for what he wanted.

'It wain't hold up, mate,' I said to him, thinking how much better it was being here than sitting in the pictures and seeing the Jungle Jim serial.

But he got nettled now and turned on me. 'Mind yer own business.'

I thought he was going to tell me to scram, but he didn't. He made ever such a fancy knot with that rope, as though he'd been a sailor or summat, and as he tied it he was whistling a fancy tune to himself. Then he got down from the table and pushed it back to the wall, and put a chair in its place. He wasn't looking black at all, nowhere near as black as anybody in our family when they're feeling fed up. If ever he'd looked only half as black as our dad looked twice a week he'd have hanged himself years ago, I couldn't help thinking. But he was making a good job of that rope all right, as though he'd thought about it a lot anyway, and as though it was going to be the last thing he'd ever do. But I knew something he didn't know, because he wasn't standing where I was. I knew the rope wouldn't hold up, and I told him so, again.

'Shut yer gob,' he said, but quiet-like, 'or I'll kick yer out.'

I didn't want to miss it, so I said nothing. He took his cap off and put it on the dresser, then he took his coat off, and his scarf, and spread them out on the sofa. I wasn't a bit frightened, like I might be now at sixteen, because it was interesting. And being only ten I'd never had a chance to see a bloke hang himself before. We got pally, the two of us, before he slipped the rope around his neck.

'Shut the door,' he asked me, and I did as I was told. 'Ye're a good lad for your age,' he said to me while I sucked my thumb, and he felt in his pockets and pulled out all that was inside, throwing the handful of bits and bobs on the table: fag-packet and peppermints, a pawn ticket, an old comb, and a few coppers. He picked out a penny and gave it to me, saying: 'Now listen ter me, young 'un. I'm going to 'ang messen, and when I'm swinging I want you to gi' this chair a bloody good kick and push it away. All right?'

I nodded.

He put the rope around his neck, and then took it off like it was a tie that didn't fit. 'What are yer going to do it for, mate?' I asked again.

'Because I'm fed up,' he said, looking very unhappy. 'And because I want to. My missus left me, and I'm out o' work.'

I didn't want to argue, because the way he said it, I knew he couldn't do anything else except hang himself. Also there was a funny look in his face: even when he talked to me I swear he couldn't see me. It was different to the black looks my old man puts on, and I suppose that's why my old man would never hang himself, worse luck, because he never gets a look into his clock like this bloke had. My old man's look stares *at* you, so that you have to back down and fly out of the house: this bloke's look looked *through* you, so that you could face it and know it wouldn't do you any harm. So I saw now that dad would never hang himself because he could never get the right sort of look into his face, in spite of the fact that he'd been out of work often enough. Maybe mam would have to leave him first, and then he might do it; but no – I shook my head – there wasn't much chance of that even though he did lead her a dog's life.

'Yer wain't forget to kick that chair away?' he reminded me, and I swung my head to say I wouldn't. So my eyes were popping and I watched every move he made. He stood on the chair and put the rope around his neck so that it fitted this time, still whistling his fancy tune. I wanted to get a better goz at the knot, because my pal was in the scouts, and would ask to know how it was done, and if I told him later he'd let me know what happened at the pictures in the Jungle Jim serial, so's I could have my cake and eat it as well, as mam says, tit for tat. But I thought I'd better not ask the bloke to tell me, and I stayed back in my corner. The last thing he did was take the wet dirty butt end from his lips and sling it into the empty firegrate, following it with his eyes to the black fireback where it landed – as if he was then going to mend a fault in the lighting like any electrician.

Suddenly his long legs wriggled and his feet tried to kick the chair, so I helped him as I'd promised I would and took a runner at it as if I was playing centre forward for Notts Forest, and the chair went scooting back against the sofa, dragging his muffler to the floor as it tipped over. He swung for a bit, his arms chafing like he was a scarecrow flapping birds away, and he made a noise in his throat as if he'd just took a dose of salts and was trying to make them stay down.

Then there was another sound, and I looked up and saw a big crack come in the ceiling, like you see on the pictures when an earthquake's happening, and the bulb began circling round and round as though it was a space ship. I was just beginning to get dizzy when, thank Christ, he fell down with such a horrible thump on the floor that I thought he'd broke every bone he'd got. He kicked around for a bit, like a dog that's got colic bad. Then he lay still.

I didn't stay to look at him. 'I told him that rope wouldn't hold up,' I kept saying to myself as I went out of the house, tut-tutting because he hadn't done the job right, hands stuffed deep into my pockets and nearly crying at the balls-up he'd made of everything. I slammed his gate so hard with disappointment that it nearly dropped off its hinges.

Just as I was going back up the yard to get my tea at home, hoping the others had come back from the pictures so's I wouldn't have anything to keep on being black about, a copper passed me and headed for the bloke's door. He was striding quickly with his head bent forward, and I knew that somebody had narked. They must have seen him buy the rope and then tipped off the cop. Or happen the old hen at the yard end had finally caught on. Or perhaps he'd even told somebody himself, because I supposed that the bloke who'd strung himself up hadn't much known what he was doing, especially with the look I'd seen in his eyes. But that's how it is, I said to myself, as I followed the copper back to the bloke's house, a poor bloke can't even hang himself these days.

When I got back the copper was slitting the rope from his neck with a penknife, then he gave him a drink of water, and the bloke opened his peepers. I didn't like the copper, because he'd got a couple of my mates sent to approved school for pinching lead piping from lavatories.

'What did you want to hang yourself for?' he asked the bloke, trying to make him sit up. He could hardly talk, and one of his hands was bleeding from where the light bulb had smashed. I knew that rope wouldn't hold up, but he hadn't listened to me. I'll never hang myself anyway, but if I want to I'll make sure I do it from a tree or something like that, not a light fitting. 'Well, what did you do it for?'

'Because I wanted to,' the bloke croaked.

'You'll get five years for this,' the copper told him. I'd crept back into the house and was sucking my thumb in the same corner.

'That's what yo' think,' the bloke said, a normal frightened look in his eyes now. 'I only wanted to hang myself.'

'Well,' the copper said, taking out his book, 'it's against the law, you know.'

'Nay,' the bloke said, 'it can't be. It's my life, ain't it?'

'You might think so,' the copper said, 'but it ain't.'

He began to suck the blood from his hand. It was such a little scratch though that you couldn't see it. 'That's the first thing I knew,' he said.

'Well I'm telling you,' the copper told him.

'Course, I didn't let on to the copper that I'd helped the bloke to hang himself. I wasn't born yesterday, nor the day before yesterday neither.

'It's a fine thing if a bloke can't tek his own life,' the bloke said, seeing he was in for it.

'Well he can't,' the copper said, as if reading out of his book and enjoying it. 'It ain't your life. And it's a crime to take your own life. It's killing yourself. It's suicide.'

The bloke looked hard, as if every one of the copper's words meant six months cold. I felt sorry for him, and that's a fact, but if only he'd listened to what I'd said and not depended on that light fitting. He should have done it from a tree, or something like that.

He went up the yard with the copper like a peaceful lamb, and we all thought that that was the end of that.

But a couple of days later the news was flashed through to us – even before it got to the *Post* because a woman in our yard worked at the hospital of an evening dishing grub out and tidying up. I heard her spilling it to somebody at the yard end. 'I'd never 'ave thought it. I thought he'd got that daft idea out of his head when they took him away. But no. Wonders'll never cease. Chucked 'issen from the hospital window when the copper who sat near his bed went off for a pee. Would you believe it? Dead? Not much 'e ain't.'

He'd heaved himself at the glass, and fallen like a stone on to the road. In one way I was sorry he'd done it, but in another I was glad, because he'd proved to the coppers and everybody whether it was his life or not all right. It was marvellous though, the way the brainless bastards had put him in a ward six floors up, which finished him off, proper, even better than a tree.

All of which will make me think twice about how black I sometimes feel. The black coal bag locked inside you, and the black look it puts on your face, doesn't mean you're going to string yourself up or sling yourself under a double-decker or chuck yourself out of a window or cut your throat with a sardine tin or put your head in the gas oven or drop your rotten sack-bag of a body on to a railway line, because when you're feeling that black you can't even move from your chair. Anyhow, I know I'll never get so black as to hang myself, because hanging don't look very nice to me, and never will, the more I remember old what's-his-name swinging from the light fitting.

More than anything else, I'm glad now I didn't go to the pictures that Saturday afternoon when I was feeling black and ready to do myself in. Because you know, I shan't ever kill myself. Trust me. I'll stay alive half barmy till I'm a hundred and five, and then go out screaming blue murder because I want to stay where I am.

Reading Aids – 3

page 44: *bloke* man.
black ill-tempered; in a bad mood.
stringing himself up hanging himself (from the slang used in films about the American wild west).
Sunday-joint maulers hands as big as joints of beef.

45 *scrunched* huddled.
broodier in a worse mood.
mashed some tea made tea, leaving it to infuse in the pot.
clink jail.
plugged motionless; stuck.
it's murder so serious that trouble is liable to break out.
summat something (northern English dialect).
the bookie's the bookmaker's shop.
fibbed lied.

46 *messen* myself (northern English dialect).
cackled on the other side of her face treated it as no laughing matter.

47 *nettled* irritated.
scram go away.
gob mouth.
bits and bobs odds and ends.

49 *clock* face.
goz look.
butt end cigarette end.
muffler scarf.
chafing flopping about.

50 *balls-up* complete mess.
narked informed the police.
peepers eyes.

51 *that's the first thing I knew* it's the first time I've known that.

52 *barmy* mad.
go out die.
screaming blue murder protesting at the top of my voice.

Study Aids – 3

Commentary: On Saturday Afternoon

Alan Sillitoe has made characterization an important aspect of this story. As the author he takes on the character of a sixteen-year-old boy who is the first-person narrator. Everything and everyone is judged according to the effect they have upon himself.

The forefront of the stage is occupied throughout by the boy, who is the only character developed in any detail. He tells us he is the victim of black moods – a characteristic of the family – and these moods are highly important and dangerous states. He is a bit of a guttersnipe in outlook and attitude. He is vulgarly critical of other people. He detests the law. His mind is conditioned partly by adventure films, and he has a strong sense of self-preservation. Throughout the story he is only the receiver of impressions about the outside world, rather than an actor, except once when he kicks away the chair from the feet of the would-bc suicide. He is no hero in the usual sense of the word: rather, what is known as an 'anti-hero'.

The other characters are not developed in any detail. The father is described briefly because of the family trait of having black moods. The suicide is just a man down on his luck, the policeman is just 'the law' and the woman is just defined as a gossip. So that the maximum emphasis will be on the experiences of the narrator, nobody, not even the narrator, is given a name. What is related stands out because of the anonymity of the people. And the facelessness of the characters also suggests a hard community in which people live their own lives without much co-operation or friendliness.

The author helps the anonymity by the absence of description. We do not know what the narrator or his father or any of the other characters look like except for a brief description of the suicide.

We are told that the narrator is a boy of sixteen and that the story he is telling happened when he was ten. Although the older and more mature narrator has some insights that the ten-year-old could not have, the difference in time is so small that the events are fresh in his mind and he is recognizably the same person as the boy who had the experiences he is recounting.

Most of the characters are drawn from the lower working class, rough, coarse, physically violent. The policeman, with his respect for the law, contrasts with the others and points up the harshness of their lives.

At the end of the story the experiences undergone by the central character have clarified his attitude towards living. He had been oppressed by the black moods which at one time seemed to him to be a possible prelude to suicide. His experience has taught him something:

'I shan't ever kill myself. Trust me. I'll stay alive half barmy till I'm a hundred and five, and then go out screaming blue murder because I want to stay where I am.'

The kind of incident chosen is going to affect the central character and it must be such as would force him to pay attention. As he is a pretty tough child the incidents are correspondingly tough.

The early part of the story establishes the nature of the black mood of which the boy is a victim. For this purpose the author introduces a number of examples of brutal or explosive physical conduct which are in contrast to the triviality of what gives rise to it: for example, throwing over of a table of pots, and catching and throwing a fly into the fire.

The later part of the story introduces incidents that are by no means trivial: they are matters of life and death. These form a setting for the black mood which make it much less significant. These are the actions that lead to a human being with a rope round his neck swinging from a ceiling. The cause is not trivial, like a packet of fags. It is important. The man has no work and his wife has left him. The incidents are such as could happen in the rough and grimy life of this neighbourhood. They are grimly realistic and tend to make the reader accept what happens as a true record of what the boy saw.

As in *A Message from the Pig-Man*, the handling of the narrative divides itself into two main parts. The exposition consists of a longish and detailed description of the kind of experiences that have made the boy what he is: this is a well disguised character sketch in which the danger of the black mood is central to the boy's life. The particular black mood of a particular Saturday afternoon is played upon by a succession of incidents which reach a climax – the suicide. It is the successful suicide, together with the memory of the unsuccessful attempt at hanging, that cause the dénouement, a new way of looking at life – acceptance of the black moods and seeing them in their proper perspective.

As the author is mainly concerned with characters, what they think, feel and do, any elaborate background would detract from the impact of the story. Thus no attempt is made to build up a careful and detailed picture of the places in which the actions take place. Instead, little details are dropped into the story and they are carefully chosen so that they are relevant to the characters and their way of life, and are appropriate to what the characters are doing. In this the author uses the father's fireside chair and the table with the pots on it, the noisy bicycle factory and the various ordinary household items of the suicide's meagre house.

Seemingly irrelevant details are nevertheless quite important in contributing to our knowledge of the life-style of the people: the pictures (cinema), the pawn shop, the football match, the jail.

The story is written in the first person as if it were someone speaking directly at an audience of some kind. (The various devices used to this end will be dealt with later.) Again, one reason for direct speech is to relieve the possible monotony of the narrative. The actual words used in the house are shown, words relevant to the dangerous black mood: mother says to father: 'What are yo' so bleddy black for?' and, with a subtle omission to indicate a different relationship, mother says to son: 'What are yo' so black for?'

A somewhat similar use is made of direct speech in the account of the attempted suicide. Sparse bits of speech are used to punctuate the preparations of the man. Interjected every now and again, they emphasize the man's determination, his indifference to this world, the boy's dispassionate attitude and the absence of any real communication between them.

The only *real* dialogue occurs between the policeman and the failed suicide. Because of the discussion, we are made to feel even sorrier for the would-be suicide; and the logical nature of the dialogue suggests the force of law and order as a contrast with the chaos of the man's life and actions.

Direct speech is also used for the woman's description of the ultimate successful suicide. Thus the crisis is expressed in actual spoken words. It should be noticed that direct speech is used almost always where there is a conflict of some kind: the direct speech serves to humanize and highlight the conflict.

The general theme of this story is the difficulty the young have in establishing for themselves a scale of values by which they can reasonably live. A more particular theme is the difficulty the boy has in coping with the 'black' mood in his father and in himself. Just how to cope is hammered into his life by this experience of the suicide. The lesson he learns is that while a man, when faced with the harshness of life, can choose to live or die as he wants, suicide is a dreadfully final escapist exercise; life is precious, its difficulties can be borne, there is little point in being dead.

Here are some additional points about this story:

1. The author adopts the *persona* of a lower working class boy of sixteen years of age. (*Persona* means the character the author has created and adopted.)
2. Because it is a story involving an intensely personal problem, the author adopts the first person narrative method of telling it.
3. In *First Confession* we saw that the age interval between the boy and the grown-up narrator resulted in a considerable difference in the narrative at different points. Here there is no great disparity between the ten-year-old boy who had the experience and the sixteen-year-old boy who is recalling the experience and relating it. The teenager does not try to distort the story, does not pretend to be someone other than an older version of the tough little ten-year-old. He appears to us as trying to be as honest and objective as possible.
4. Nevertheless, there are two points of view in the story. The first deals with the actual remembered incidents that constitute the main action of the story as it occurred to the young boy. The

other concerns itself with the thoughts and perceptions of the older boy; he outlines the family situation that is unchanging, or he makes comments or draws conclusions with the hindsight of events.

5. Thus in the method of narration we have two strands: a vivid eye-witness blow-by-blow account of the various episodes of the experience, punctuated by the explanations of a commentator.
6. We should not miss the humorous aspect of the narration, partly arising from a tough, unsentimental view of the world, partly because of the brash *naïveté* of the boy himself.

Here now are some points about the language of the story:

1. Since the story is told in the first person narrative style, the author has to make sure that what he writes has something of the authentic quality of speech. To gain the authenticity he employs a number of devices. At times there are *colloquial forms* such as 'ain't', 'can't', 'it's', 'there's' or ''course'. At other times there are conversation 'fillers' such as 'well' or 'I suppose' or 'you see'.
2. The sentence structure is kept very simple, as in speech, with numerous short sentences. Where there are longer sentences, the parts are joined by the simplest conjunctions such as 'and', 'but', 'or' and 'so'. There is also frequent use of minor sentences. Speech is also suggested by the use of the familiar and intimate terms 'mam' and 'dad'.
3. The author also uses his language skills to establish the social status of the boy, the part of the country he comes from and the defects of his education. Both in the narrative and in the dialogues use is made of a Nottinghamshire type of speech (as you would notice from the *Reading Aids*). But the character of the narrator is further revealed by the ungrammatical writing: for example, 'he ain't got', 'He'd just took', 'were moving more natural now', 'that's got colic bad'. Notice, too, how effective the use of 'bloody' is in revealing the boy's character.
4. Much of the provincial flavour of the story comes over in the direct speech. The author tries to convey the sound of the words in the dialect used: for example, 'bleddy', 'tek', 'yer', 'yo'. This is especially effective in the dialogue between the policeman and the suicide, where the seriousness of the legal side is partly conveyed by the more normal English speech of the policeman as against the dialect of the suicide.

The tone of the story is hard, unsentimental, dispassionate. The writer is content mainly to chronicle, not to be censorious. Occasionally there are touches of humour but it is of a wry kind that derives not from the personality of the writer but from the difference between what is said and the nature of the event being told.

Although the most vivid episode of the story is an attempt at suicide we should not be misled into thinking that this is most important. The story pattern is concerned with the succession of experiences that befell the ten-year-old boy and their effect upon his life. Thus the writer spends a lot of time upon the affliction of the boy (and father) – the black mood. The boy's hasty exit as a result of his father's mood initiates the series of happenings involving members of the public outside the home, so that the black mood is given its proper place in relation to matters of life and death.

Projections – 3

1. Imagine you saw two people arguing and then having a fight. Make a list of words of your own particular local dialect and use them in your account of what happened. This could be done as a group activity. One or two group members could concentrate on one 'side' and the others on the opposite 'side' in the argument.
2. Write out a brief dialogue between a Cockney and a Scotsman (or any other pair of people from different parts of the country) after a drawn game at Wembley. Try to convey the sounds of the words each makes when talking by means of the spelling of the words, the punctuation, and so on. You could pair up with a classmate for this, each inventing the speech of one of the speakers.
3. As the narrator of *On Saturday Afternoon*, you are writing a letter to a 'mate' who is in hospital. Tell him all about what happened.
4. Imagine you are a new resident in the district in which the story is set. Use only details in the story you like, and give an account of the place and its kind of people. Then invent another story in the same setting, but make it a funny one.
5. From the evidence in the story make a short character sketch of the boy. If you like, you could also try to describe his appearance as you imagine it.
6. What is the importance of the father in the development of the story? Has the mother any importance? Would the effect of the story on the reader be different if the father and mother were different?
7. Study the points made about the language of *On Saturday Afternoon* in the Study Aids. Choose some other story you have read and try to make similar points about its language.
8. This story might make a good short film. Along with some friends, you could write a film-script for it. Here is a beginning, to show you how to do it:

Shot	*Picture*	*Sound*
1	LS typical living room in a council house. Dad slumped in a chair by the fire.	Dad: 'Crikey! Blimey! 'No fags!'
2	CU Dad looking grumpy.	
3	MS Mam scowling	Mam: 'What are yo' lookin' so bleddy black for?'
4	MS Dad catching a fly.	Dad: 'Got yer!'

(LS: Long Shot: you can see the whole of a person within the frame.
CU: Close Up: the face fills the frame.
MS: Medium Shot: you see a figure from the waist up.)

You Should Have Seen the Mess
by Muriel Spark

I am now more than glad that I did not pass into the grammar school five years ago, although it was a disappointment at the time. I was always good at English, but not so good at the other subjects!!

I am glad that I went to the secondary modern school, because it was only constructed the year before. Therefore, it was much more hygienic than the grammar school. The secondary modern was light and airy, and the walls were painted with a bright, washable gloss. One day, I was sent over to the grammar school, with a note for one of the teachers, and you should have seen the mess! The corridors were dusty, and I saw dust on the window ledges, which were chipped. I saw into one of the classrooms. It was very untidy in there.

I am also glad that I did not go to the grammar school, because of what it does to one's habits. This may appear to be a strange remark, at first sight. It is a good thing to have an education behind you, and I do not believe in ignorance, but I have had certain experiences, with educated people, since going out into the world.

I am seventeen years of age, and left school two years ago last month. I had my A certificate for typing, so got my first job, as a junior, in a solicitor's office. Mum was pleased at this, and Dad said it was a first-class start, as it was an old-established firm. I must say that when I went for the interview, I was surprised at the windows, and the stairs up to the offices were also far from clean. There was a little waiting-room, where some of the elements were missing from the gas fire, and the carpet on the floor was worn. However, Mr. Heygate's office, into which I was shown for the interview, was better. The furniture was old, but it was polished, and there was a good carpet, I will say that. The glass of the bookcase was very clean.

I was to start on the Monday, so along I went. They took me to the general office, where there were two senior shorthand-typists, and a clerk, Mr. Gresham, who was far from smart in appearance. You should have seen the mess!! There was no floor covering whatsoever, and so dusty everywhere. There were shelves all round the room, with old box files on them. The box files were falling to pieces, and all the old papers inside them were crumpled. The worst shock

TATE + LYLE
2 lb granulated sugar

of all was the tea-cups. It was my duty to make tea, mornings and afternoons. Miss Bewlay showed me where everything was kept. It was kept in an old orange box, and the cups were all cracked. There were not enough saucers to go round, etc. I will not go into the facilities, but they were also far from hygienic. After three days, I told Mum, and she was upset, most of all about the cracked cups. We never keep a cracked cup, but throw it out, because those cracks can harbour germs. So Mum gave me my own cup to take to the office.

Then at the end of the week, when I got my salary, Mr. Heygate said, 'Well, Lorna, what are you going to do with your first pay?' I did not like him saying this, and I nearly passed a comment, but I said, 'I don't know.' He said, 'What do you do in the evenings, Lorna? Do you watch Telly?' I did take this as an insult, because we call it TV, and his remark made me out to be uneducated. I just stood, and did not answer, and he looked surprised. Next day, Saturday, I told Mum and Dad about the facilities, and we decided I should not go back to that job. Also, the desks in the general office were rickety. Dad was indignant, because Mr. Heygate's concern was flourishing, and he had letters after his name.

Everyone admires our flat, because Mum keeps it spotless, and Dad keeps doing things to it. He had done it up all over, and got permission from the Council to re-modernize the kitchen. I well recall the Health Visitor, remarking to Mum, 'You could eat off your floor, Mrs. Merrifield.' It is true that you could eat your lunch off Mum's floors, and any hour of the day or night you will find every corner spick and span.

Next, I was sent by the agency to a publisher's for an interview, because of being good at English. One look was enough!! My next interview was a success, and I am still at Low's Chemical Co. It is a modern block, with a quarter of an hour rest period, morning and afternoon. Mr. Marwood is very smart in appearance. He is well spoken, although he has not got a university education behind him. There is special lighting over the desks, and the typewriters are the latest models.

So I am happy at Low's. But I have met other people, of an educated type, in the past year, and it has opened my eyes. It so happened that I had to go to the doctor's house, to fetch a prescription for my young brother, Trevor, when the epidemic was on. I rang the bell, and Mrs. Darby came to the door. She was small, with fair hair, but too long, and a green maternity dress. But she was very nice to me. I had to wait in their living-room, and you should have seen the state it was in! There were broken toys on the carpet, and the ash trays were full up. There were contemporary pictures on the walls, but the furniture was not contemporary, but old-fashioned, with covers which were past standing up to another wash, I should say. To cut a long story short, Dr. Darby and Mrs. Darby have always been very kind to me, and they meant everything for the best. Dr. Darby is also short and fair, and they have three children, a girl and a boy, and now a baby boy.

When I went that day for the prescription, Dr. Darby said to me, 'You look pale, Lorna. It's the London atmosphere. Come on a picnic with us, in the car, on Saturday.' After that I went with the Darbys more and more. I liked them, but I did not like the mess, and it was a surprise. But I also kept in with them for the opportunity of meeting people, and Mum and Dad were pleased that I had made nice friends. So I did not say anything about the cracked lino, and the paintwork all chipped. The children's clothes were very shabby for a doctor, and she changed them out of their school clothes when they came home from school, into those worn-out garments. Mum always kept us spotless to go out to play, and I do not like to say it, but those Darby children frequently looked like the Leary family, which the Council evicted from our Block, as they were far from houseproud.

One day, when I was there, Mavis (as I called Mrs. Darby by then) put her head out of the window, and shouted to the boy, 'John, stop peeing over the cabbages at once. Pee on the lawn.' I did not know which way to look. Mum would never say a word like that from the window, and I know for a fact that Trevor would never pass water outside, not even bathing in the sea.

I went there usually at the week-ends, but sometimes on weekdays, after supper. They had an idea to make a match for me with a chemist's assistant, whom they had taken up too. He was an orphan, and I do not say there was anything wrong with that. But he was not accustomed to those little extras that I was. He was a good-looking boy, I will say that. So I went once to a dance, and twice to films with him. To look at, he was quite clean in appearance. But there was only hot water at the week-end at his place, and he said that a bath once a week was sufficient. Jim (as I called Dr. Darby by then) said it was sufficient also, and surprised me. He did not have much money, and I do not hold that against him. But there was no hurry for me, and I could wait for a man in a better position, so that I would not miss those little extras. So he started going out with a girl from the coffee bar, and did not come to the Darbys very much then.

There were plenty of boys at the office, but I will say this for the Darbys, they had lots of friends coming and going, and they had interesting conversation, although sometimes it gave me a surprise, and I did not know where to look. And sometimes they had people who were very down and out, although there is no need to be. But most of the guests were different, so it made a comparison with the boys at the office, who were not so educated in their conversation.

Now it was near the time for Mavis to have her baby, and I was to come in at the week-end, to keep an eye on the children, while the help had her day off. Mavis did not go away to have her baby, but would have it at home, in their double bed, as they did not have twin beds, although he was a doctor. A girl I knew, in our block, was engaged, but was let down, and even she had her baby in the labour ward. I was sure the bedroom was not hygienic for having a baby, but I did not mention it.

One day, after the baby boy came along, they took me in the car to the country, to see Jim's mother. The baby was put in a carry-cot at the back of the car. He began to cry, and without a word of a lie, Jim said to him over his shoulder, 'Oh shut your gob, you little bastard.' I did not know what to do, and Mavis was smoking a cigarette. Dad would not dream of saying such a thing to Trevor or I. When we arrived at Jim's mother's place, Jim said, 'It's a fourteenth-century cottage, Lorna.' I could well believe it. It was very

cracked and old, and it made one wonder how Jim could let his old mother live in this tumble-down cottage, as he was so good to everyone else. So Mavis knocked at the door, and the old lady came. There was not much anyone could do to the inside. Mavis said, 'Isn't it charming, Lorna?' If that was a joke, it was going too far. I said to the old Mrs. Darby, 'Are you going to be re-housed?' but she did not understand this, and I explained how you have to apply to the Council, and keep at them. But it was funny that the Council had not done something already, when they go round condemning. Then old Mrs. Darby said, 'My dear, I shall be re-housed in the Grave.' I did not know where to look.

There was a carpet on the wall, which I think was there to hide a damp spot. She had a good TV set, I will say that. But some of the walls were bare brick, and the facilities were outside, through the garden. The furniture was far from new.

One Saturday afternoon, as I happened to go to the Darbys, they were just going off to a film and they took me too. It was the Curzon, and afterwards we went to a flat in Curzon Street. It was a very clean Block, I will say that, and there were good carpets at the entrance. The couple there had contemporary furniture, and they also spoke about music. It was a nice place, but there was no Welfare Centre to the flats, where people could go for social intercourse, advice, and guidance. But they were well-spoken, and I met Willy Morley, who was an artist. Willy sat beside me, and we had a drink. He was young, dark, with a dark shirt, so one could not see right away if he was clean. Soon after this, Jim said to me, 'Willy wants to paint you, Lorna. But you'd better ask your Mum.' Mum said it was all right if he was a friend of the Darbys.

I can honestly say that Willy's place was the most unhygienic place I have seen in my life. He said I had an unusual type of beauty, which he must capture. This was when we came back to his place from the restaurant. The light was very dim, but I could see the bed had not been made, and the sheets were far from clean. He said he must paint me, but I told Mavis I did not like to go back there. 'Don't you like Willy?' she asked. I could not deny that I liked Willy, in a way. There was something about him, I will say that. Mavis said, 'I hope he hasn't been making a pass at you, Lorna.' I said he had not done so, which was almost true, because he did not attempt to go to the full extent. It was always unhygienic when I went to Willy's place, and I told him so once, but he said, 'Lorna, you are a joy.' He had a nice way, and he took me out in his car, which was a good one, but dirty inside, like his place. Jim said one day, 'He has pots of money, Lorna,' and Mavis said, 'You might make a man of him, as he is keen on you.' They always said Willy came from a good family.

But I saw that one could not do anything with him. He would not change his shirt very often, or get clothes, but he went round like a tramp, lending people money, as I have seen with my own eyes. His place was in a terrible mess, with the empty bottles, and laundry in the corner. He gave me several gifts over the period, which I took as he would have only given them away, but he never tried to go to the full extent. He never painted my portrait, as he was painting fruit on a table all that time, and they said his pictures were marvellous, and thought Willy and I were getting married.

One night, when I went home, I was upset as usual, after Willy's place. Mum and Dad had gone to bed, and I looked round our kitchen which is done in primrose and white. Then I went into the living-room, where Dad has done one wall in a patterned paper, deep rose and white, and the other walls pale rose, with white woodwork. The suite is new, and Mum keeps everything beautiful. So it came to me, all of a sudden, what a fool I was, going with Willy. I agree to equality, but as to me marrying Willy, as I said to Mavis, when I recall his place, and the good carpet gone greasy, not to mention the paint oozing out of the tubes, I think it would break my heart to sink so low.

Reading Aids – 4

page 59: *secondary modern* a school to which pupils went after failing the 'eleven plus' examination.
more hygienic cleaner.
a junior typists were classed as 'senior' and 'junior', a junior being one with little or no office experience.
elements parts of an electric or gas fire that give out heat.
box files boxes in which business papers were kept.

61 *facilities* 'polite' way of saying 'toilets' or 'lavatories'.
the agency a private employment agency.
epidemic a fast-spreading disease such as influenza.

62 *kept in with them* was friendly, in a kind of subservient way.
evicted put out of the rented house for non-payment of rent or rates.
make a match bring people together so that marriage will result.

63 *was let down* the man did not marry the woman to whom he was engaged and who was bearing his child.
gob mouth.

64 *carpet on the wall* she does not recognize that it is a tapestry.

Study Aids – 4

Commentary: You Should Have Seen the Mess

Muriel Spark's central aim in this story is the creation of an individual character. The title *You Should Have Seen the Mess* has an underlying meaning. It refers not only to one of that girl's favourite phrases, it is also a description of the values by which she lives her life.

The main character, Lorna, is revealed in considerable detail as a pretty, self-satisfied, egotistical, gossipy female prig. At seventeen years of age, when girls are still coming to terms with the world, she is quite convinced she knows everything and that she is always right.

All the other characters are presented as seen through Lorna's eyes and are distorted by her peculiar outlook and scale of values, except for her 'Mum' and 'Dad' who can do no wrong in her eyes. Any boy who does not fit into her own pattern for living is rejected. Only once does another character awaken a response of feeling in her, giving her the chance to become a vital human being, but he is dismissed because he does not measure up to her standards of cleanliness.

In making Lorna sketch herself, the author has tried not to weight the evidence too strongly against her. Thus the reader is left undecided as to whether to laugh and to condemn or whether to feel sad at the waste of life.

To bring out the narrowness of Lorna's scale of values the author makes her meet and be acted on by a wide range of people – business colleagues, friends, possible husbands. No matter how diverse they are, she reacts in the same fashion to all of them. Thus the normal action and re-action of characters in a short story is here replaced by a stream of people whose actions have no chance of changing the life of the heroine. In a kind of paradox the most important experience she has only results in her clinging more firmly to her narrow outlook on life. She is not changed by life, she changes life to suit herself.

Although the primary interest is the revelation of character, this is achieved by exposing Lorna to successive incidents which inspire her to make judgments. These incidents range over a fairly wide section of life. They all offend her sense of propriety. They are mainly crowded into a time-span of two years after leaving school, so that each incident is used either to underline some trait of personality already known or to introduce still another trait.

All the actions, whether they are important or unimportant, are made to seem of the same significance because of her attitude.

The story is primarily concerned with characterization. The character of the central figure does not change, so in this case the initial situation is in fact her character and the complications are all the experiences that bring out or test her character. So the author places her in a variety of situations culminating in the affair with Willy. For once, her heart is to some extent engaged. But love, normally a powerful agent in the life of a seventeen-year-old girl, withers before her narrow principles. In the dénouement we see the triumph of her philosophy of life, a terrifyingly barren one, symbolized by a spick and span kitchen and living room, hygienic but cold.

Because of the character of Lorna, backgrounds are quite an important aspect of the story. The author uses the girl's home to fix the setting which so dominates her judgment that she uses it as a yardstick for all other places. Since opposition of some kind is of the essence in a good story, a succession of backgrounds is provided. Each one has features that offend Lorna in some way: dirt in the grammar school; gas fires, carpets and chipped cups in an office; oozing paint tubes and grease on the carpet in an artist's studio.

One particular use of background should be noticed. When she is faced with the fourteenth-century cottage, Lorna's application of her genteel standards result in her being, unconsciously, a figure of fun, if not also of contempt. Here the background serves to reveal her limitations in taste, knowledge and common sense.

It is clear that background is important in the revelation of character because the physical condition of places is more important to her than people are. It is only a victory for her snobbery that makes her overlook the 'defects' of the doctor's establishment.

Since the story is told as by Lorna in the first person, the way in which the author makes her speak is important for the revelation of the kind of person she is. There is remarkably little dialogue in the story, and not much speech of any kind. We can assume, therefore, that when speech does occur, the author has some special reason for using it.

Snatches of remembered speech have stuck in Lorna's mind, and these snatches give an insight into her character. Also, they enliven the schoolgirlish narrative with touches of realism. Sometimes the bits of speech contribute to her established values; sometimes they deeply offend her shallow taste. On two occasions only is speech used rather more extensively, both times with telling effect. The first is at the fourteenth-century cottage of old Mrs Darby where Lorna makes a fool of herself; the other is the highly significant affair with Willy where the basic elements of the relationship are put into bits of direct speech.

The theme of this story is based on the adoption by a child of very narrow principles of taste and judgment and the effect on her life at home, at business, with friends, and when touched by love. The author does not judge Lorna, but leaves it to the reader to decide whether her principles and the application of them make her a comic or a tragic figure.

For this purpose the first-person form of narration is very suitable. It allows her to describe her experiences and to reveal her qualities of mind and heart by giving her comments. Muriel Spark is extraordinarily clever at assuming the persona of a seventeen-year-old girl, carefully selecting those things she can praise and those things she can condemn: so that, while in the first few paragraphs the basis of her character is laid, each successive episode adds another touch to the character sketch. It expands and becomes more rounded the further we go in the story.

Whereas in *First Confession* and *On Saturday Afternoon* we were aware of two 'different' people in the story, the narrator and his earlier self who was the participator in the events, in this story we are aware of only one person. This is partly because most of the events cover only two years, but it is also because the narrator has really learned nothing new from her experiences; as she was at secondary modern school so is she after her affair with Willy the artist.

Since character is important in this story and since it is first-person narration, the kind of language used affects our estimate of what Lorna is. After all, she is speaking to us and, as in life, we learn much from the language used in communicating with us. Lorna self-confidently asserts that she is good at English. In fact the author makes her lapse into a great number of the common mistakes that are the mark of a not-too-clever person who has not been able to take advantage of teaching. She concon-stantly breaks the rules for good writing and speaking and sometimes objects to uses of English that are expressive and acceptable. Some of the mistakes are such as could not occur in anyone brought up in a home where the English language was used competently. The sentence structures show all kinds of errors while the intrusion of irrelevant thoughts into the narrative are meant as a pointer to an untidy mind.

Much of the vocabulary she is made to use is of the colloquially tarnished kind such as 'nice' and 'terrible'. She has a stock of clichés ready at hand to apply to every situation she meets: for example, 'I will say that',

'To cut a long story short', 'I did not know which way to look', and so on.

It is the consistently weak English that ties the whole story together effectively. Not only does it appear to be original, and certainly unusual, but it shows an unchanging mind applying itself in a limited way to changing circumstances.

Muriel Spark makes brilliant use of 'I' to reveal a narrow, egotistical point of view. This may be seen from the thoughts expressed at the openings of the first three paragraphs.

The author establishes the character of Lorna very quickly. Thereafter, in keeping with her character and ability, we are given a series of reminiscences, each with its highlights, each showing her in action in different phases of her life and reaching a kind of climax in her affair with Willy. In the end she is back where all the damage to her had been done, at home.

Projections – 4

1. Make better English of:
   'The worst shock of all was the tea-cups. It was my duty to make tea, mornings and afternoons. Miss Bewlay showed me where everything was kept. It was kept in an old orange box, and the cups were all cracked. There were not enough saucers to go round, etc. I will not go into the facilities, but they were also far from hygienic.'
2. Make a list of some of the cliché phrases or sayings used by Lorna. Using a selection, write a short first-person narrative piece as if you were Lorna. This could then form the basis for a dramatic monologue or stage sketch, complete with stage directions. One possible setting is Lorna in the small hall of her home, speaking to a friend on the telephone.
3. Imagine Willy has been told by Lorna that the affair is over. He is annoyed and writes a character sketch that shows his annoyance. Write this, trying to capture Willy's rather 'posh' speech.
4. Write out 'Lorna's Ten Commandments for Behaviour'. Each will begin 'Thou shalt not . . .' Then write out ten beginning 'Thou shalt . . .'
5. 'I am so glad that I did not go to grammar school because of what it does to one's habits.' Give an account of what occurs in the story to give her this impression of educated people.
6. Discuss the friendship of the Darbys with Lorna and how important it was to the girl.
7. Imagine a conversation between Lorna and the boy in *On Saturday Afternoon*. Try to capture the distinctive speech habits of each, and try to show how the boy shocks Lorna by his vulgarity. This could be written as a short story or as a play. Choose a suitable setting for the action – for example, they might meet at a dance, or in a bus.

8. Create a dialogue between Dr Darby and his wife as they discuss Lorna. Mrs Darby might be criticizing the girl for her narrow-mindedness while the doctor defends her by explaining the reasons why Lorna is what she is. The commentary in STUDY AIDS – 4 will give you material for both points of view.
9. Form a group of four, each member choosing a character from a story in this book. Play the 'balloon game'. You are all in a balloon in the air which is in danger of crashing. One has to get out to lighten the load. Each one tries to make a case for staying in because he or she is a more useful member of society than the others.
10. Choose a short story from another book, or a chapter from a novel. Write a commentary on it, using the headings and terms introduced in STUDY AIDS – 1.

Acknowledgements

The editor and publishers wish to thank the following for permission to reprint copyright material:

Curtis Brown Ltd for 'A Message from the Pig Man' by John Wain; A. D. Peters for 'First Confession' by Frank O'Connor from *Stories of Frank O'Connor*; W. H. Allen for 'On Saturday Afternoon' by Alan Sillitoe. A full selection of Sillitoe stories is published by Longmans in the Imprint Book Series. An associated cassette of Alan Sillitoe's reading of 'On Saturday Afternoon' is also available from Longmans; Harold Ober Associates Incorporated for 'You Should Have Seen The Mess' by Muriel Spark from *The Go-Away Bird*.